# Holding on to Mamie

## MY MOTHER, DEMENTIA AND ME

ELIZABETH MURRAY

HOLDING ON TO MAMIE

Published by Park Place Press
Winnipeg, Manitoba

Printed and bound in Canada by Friesens
Altona, Manitoba, Canada

ISBN: 978-1-77136-343-3

In loving memory of my mother, Ellen May ("Mamie") Murray

Do not go gentle into that good night,
Old age should burn and rave at close of day;
Rage, rage against the dying of the light.

*Dylan Thomas, 1914-1953*

# Preface

IN 2011, 747,000 Canadians 65 years of age or older were living with Alzheimer's disease, the most common form of dementia. As baby boomers age and people live longer, the Alzheimer's Society of Canada predicts that 1.4 million will be living with the disease by 2031.

The numbers are astounding, yet in 2004 when my mother was diagnosed, I didn't recognize dementia and I wasn't prepared for the changes in her personality as her illness strengthened its hold. I believed that dementia was simply the medical term for the lapses of memory that frequently occur with normal aging. I didn't realize that impaired judgment, paranoia and depression were other common symptoms of the disease.

In hindsight it's easy to see the early signs of my mother's illness, but at the time I wasn't looking for trouble. I was dealing with my own health issues and overlooked the linkage between seemingly unrelated events. I didn't want to believe that dementia was lurking; I preferred to dismiss my mother's behaviour as normal and ignore the possibility of more serious implications. Perhaps if I had been better informed about the disease I wouldn't have been so ashamed when my mother turned against me. I might have been less confused about what was happening to her and to our relationship. I might have been willing to talk to more people and to disclose the hurt that her illness inflicted.

My mother's disease strained already contentious relationships. I have tried to include only the information that was necessary to properly explain our family dynamic and some of my feelings and frustrations during my mother's cognitive decline. To protect their privacy, I have changed the names of some family members.

This book was a work in progress for several years. I would write a little and then stop, often for many months. It was my mother's notes that continually brought me back to my project and motivated me to keep going. The notes are tangible evidence of how my mother interpreted people and events as her illness progressed, offering unique insight into the effects of dementia.

Dementia attacks the very essence of its victims. It affects families and relationships in ways that other illnesses do not. Caring for a loved one with dementia will never be easy but by sharing my experience, I hope that others will feel a little less bewildered, a little less alone as they embark on their own battle against the disease.

# Chapter One

**WEDGEWOOD DRIVE INTERSECTED** Thatcher Drive directly in front of my mother's house, a twelve hundred-square-foot, three bedroom split-level in the south end of Winnipeg, built when most of the neighbourhood was still open field. My parents were its first owners and my mother had lived there for nearly forty-seven years. When I was young I liked to pretend that the entire length of Wedgewood was our driveway, like a promenade leading to a grand palace. Now, as I turned off University Crescent, I used the long approach to try to make sense of the vendetta that my mother had launched against me. It had been months since she had left me unattended in her house and I was apprehensive about what I would find.

When I stepped into the small foyer, the house felt eerily quiet but not abandoned, as if my mother was sleeping in an upstairs room. A bookcase and a sheet of gold Plexiglas separated the foyer from the L-shaped living room and dining room. The pony wall had been one of my mother and father's do-it-yourself projects and it still rattled whenever the front door was firmly shut. In recent months, my mother had placed a pair of my father's shoes in a prominent position in the entry, even though he had been dead for almost fourteen years.

Green and gold damask wallpaper covered the front hall and the stair wall leading to the second floor. In the living room, lamps with dangling crystal prisms and marble-topped end tables flanked the sofa. I remembered when my mother had wanted to give the living room a facelift in the early 1970s, but my parents didn't purchase anything unless they had the money in hand and the family budget hadn't allowed for an elaborate makeover.

Soon after I entered Grade Seven, my mother started working in the customer service department of the Simpson Sears store at Polo Park Shopping Centre. For months, she set aside a portion of her paycheque while she considered wallpaper and carpet samples and deliberated over the selection of couches and armchairs. Decorating those rooms with money she had earned had given her a sense of accomplishment – a reminder of the independent career woman she had once been.

A pocket door led from the living room to the kitchen. A bowl, mug and side plate resting in the drying rack beside the sink confirmed that my mother had washed the dishes after her last breakfast in her home. A stack of clothes in varying stages of repair balanced precariously on the sewing machine in the corner. Scrawled reminder notes and newspaper articles were taped to the cupboard doors and on the wall beside the phone. My mother had taught my son, Davis, to use the black rotary dial when he was just four years old, guiding his index finger into the appropriate holes and gently rotating his hand so he could call 9-1-1 if the need ever arose.

I pulled open the refrigerator door. Bags of cookies and several packages of mini chocolate bars were crammed into the produce drawer. A box containing half a dozen stale, maple-glazed donuts had usurped the space on the top shelf where a jug of milk had always been found. My mother rarely refused an offer of dessert but even after my father had died and she was cooking for one, she had made sure that she had at least one proper meal a day. She would regularly prepare a chicken breast or pork chop along with rice or a boiled potato and whatever other vegetable she had in her crisper. Now, the closest thing to nutritious food on the bare shelves was a hardened block of cheddar cheese covered in a thick layer of turquoise mould.

It had been almost a year since I had been allowed upstairs. In the master bedroom, my mother's silver-backed hairbrush and mirror rested neatly in their tray on her dresser; only the ballerina lamp that had once been mine occupied her night table. I opened the top drawer of the long, low bureau. The smell of lavender sachets tucked among the stacks of jewellery was an instant reminder of the many Sunday afternoons I had spent as a child, stretched out on my parents' double bed with the sun streaming in the window and a pile of velvet covered boxes by my side. My mother's only precious jewellery was her engagement ring and an emerald ring that my father had given her for their twenty-fifth wedding anniversary but she had a large collection of costume pieces, most of which she had acquired before she was married.

I would carefully lift a bracelet or necklace or brooch from its container, twisting and turning it until its reflection danced across the ceiling. Sometimes, I would layer pieces one on top of the other until I was laden with glitter. I cherished the times when my mother sat on the bed beside me and told me the stories that accompanied each piece of sparkling metal. "A guy I knew in Cobourg gave me this," she would say with a mysterious smile, or, "I wore this to a dance in Oshawa."

My mother and father didn't have an active social life when I was a child but for many years they did go to a New Year's Eve dance at the Air Force Base with Dick and Anne Sutton. My mother would make herself a new dress for the occasion, finishing the last details just minutes before their scheduled departure. I would follow her from her bedroom to the bathroom and marvel at how beautiful she looked as she quickly slipped into her dress and adjusted her hair and make-up. She was naturally slim; her long arms and legs made her appear taller than her five-foot-seven-inch frame. She had broad shoulders, narrow hips, and well-toned calves that tapered to slender ankles. Her ash blond hair and pale blue eyes made up for her nose, which was a little too large for her otherwise delicate features.

My bedroom was located at the back of the house, tucked behind the bathroom. As the smallest of the three bedrooms, it lacked in size but my mother had ensured that I had a sanctuary of coordinating wallpaper, bed linen and drapery. We would study the pages of beautifully appointed bedrooms in the Eaton's department store catalogue before selecting a colour scheme and style. Over the years, pink ballerinas gave way to purple gingham, which in turn was replaced by green chiffon frills. The existing blue and white striped wallpaper arrived with new furniture and the requisite matching bedding the summer before I had started Grade Eleven.

"I would have loved a room like this when I was your age," my mother would tell me wistfully after each new look was complete. Whether it was a beautiful bedroom, dance lessons or a new sweater, my mother always gave me the things that she had been deprived of when she was a child.

Until recently, my mother had maintained my room exactly as it had been when I moved out of the house. The drawers beneath the bed contained a selection of well-worn t-shirts and sweaters; my bookshelf displayed several textbooks from law school, and the bulletin board above my desk still held old ticket stubs, receipts and an Inuit art calendar from 1987. My husband, Jeff, liked to tease my mother that she kept my room as a shrine, hoping that I would someday return and reclaim it as my own. "You just never know," she would respond with a smile.

My former retreat was now an odd jumble of paper and assorted debris, including two old lamps, a broken desk chair and an end table that I had last seen in the basement. The bed had become a repository for a stack of flannel bed sheets that were so faded the once vibrant patterns were barely visible; a laundry basket was full of odds and ends, including an old toaster and several cardboard boxes. Three battered suitcases were wedged between the bed and the mirrored doors of the closet. The luggage was part of a set that my mother had purchased prior to her honeymoon in 1958 and had long been relegated to the crawl space over the kitchen and living room. The exquisitely illustrated children's books that I had accumulated during my student years when I had worked part time in a bookstore had disappeared.

A shoebox on the closet shelf caught my eye. It held an unfamiliar pair of feather-embellished mules and a note written in the margin of a grocery store flyer.

*Liz said these were a waste of money and she wouldn't be caught dead wearing them*

My hand trembled as I closed the lid, worried about what I might find in the next drawer, bag or box. I began to scour the house, opening cupboards, drawers and closets. Masses of correspondence had been stuffed into dressers, desks and buffets. Additional papers were jammed into boxes or bags and hidden under the beds. The piles of paper contained an assortment of newspapers, clippings, letters, magazines and other miscellaneous scraps of paper. Important documents such as property tax bills and income tax receipts were mixed with long-expired coupons. Notes in my mother's handwriting were everywhere, written on lined notepaper, on bits and pieces torn from a flyer or newspaper, in the margins of letters and documents, and scrawled on used envelopes that had been torn open to provide a larger writing surface. Some of the notes seemed to be my mother's attempt to make sense of what was happening around her; some were likely intended to be scripts for conversations with my brother or another willing listener. Others were drafts of letters that outlined her countless concerns. Virtually all of the notes had something negative to say about me.

Their existence didn't come as a complete surprise. In the last two years, I had spotted several lying casually on the coffee table or the kitchen counter. Once, I had managed to palm an already crumpled envelope when my mother wasn't looking and sneak it into the bathroom to read. That message began with a bitter condemnation: *Liz has always been so full of spite.* I had wondered how she had carried so much fury and fear and why she had been so determined to destroy any evidence of her love for me.

When I was growing up, my mother had never acknowledged my flaws to anyone; she had vociferously defended everything I said or did if anyone else dared to criticize. More recently, her attitude towards me had changed dramatically and while her written accusations only echoed the angry verbal recriminations I had already endured, the sheer volume of the notes left me feeling battered and confused.

I took the time to read some of the vitriolic contents, gasping at my mother's skewed view of things I had said and done. A message on a scrap of loose-leaf hidden between the pages of one of her favourite cookbooks was almost more than I could bear.

> Wanda Francey convinced me to go to Alter Guild last night. Haven't been since I lost couldn't drive anymore and wanted to know WHY. Told them about Kalanansky and how she hates me. Betty asked what my daughter thought about it all. Told her all Liz can do is gloat she's so HAPPY about the whole thing. NO HELP AT ALL!! Said she's likely behind it all anyway.
>
> I KNOW HOW TO GET BACK AT HER

I tore the paper into tinier and tinier pieces, as if destroying my mother's words would protect me from her anger. Desperate to make sense of her bitter indictment, I slowly began to organize her notes into a sort of diary – a chronology of my mother's cognitive decline. As I worked, wisps of near and distant memories whirled around in my mind like a windstorm. I was frantically looking for something to hold onto, anything that would corroborate what I had always believed – that my mother and I had shared a close and loving relationship.

# Chapter Two

**MY MOTHER'S NAME** was Mamie Murray for almost fifty years but in all that time she still thought of herself as a Winstanley. Her parents, Gilbert Winstanley and Elizabeth Mary Sutton, met in England just after the end of the First World War. Grandpa was engaged to one of Grandma's younger sisters, but Grandma, who was older than Grandpa by several years, set her sights on him and persuaded him that she was the better choice. With the help of another sister, the pair eloped and immigrated to Canada, causing a rift in Grandma's family that never healed.

The couple moved to Campbellford, Ontario, a small town midway between Toronto and Ottawa where Grandpa worked in the pulp and paper mill. Grandma, who had trained as a nurse in England, shared her medical knowledge with anyone who couldn't afford to visit the town doctor, and even some who could.

Their first child, Peter, was born in the spring of 1920. My mother followed on May 7, 1921. She was officially named Ellen May, but when Peter first learned to talk, he called his baby sister *May May*. *May May* evolved into *May-me*, and the name stuck.

Peter had been born prematurely and was often ill. Grandma spent a lot of time caring for him and as a result, my mother was left to fend for herself. Peter had largely outgrown his health issues by the time he started school but Grandma continued to pamper and spoil her only son. When money was scarce, Grandma and Grandpa would scrimp and save to buy one bicycle, one pair of skates or one tennis racquet – always for Peter.

When Peter was older, he sold the family's extra vegetables from a cart in the centre of town. Although my mother was frequently recruited to help her brother in his business venture, the profits were always his. My mother said she never minded when Peter was given things that she wasn't; she maintained that she was tougher than her brother and she was happy to do without.

My mother often told me tales about roller skating fearlessly down the slope in front of her house on Church Street or tobogganing down the daredevil track on Horkin's Hill, the ridge at the rear of their property. Her eyes lit up whenever she recalled riding her horse bareback or sneaking Smut, the family's black lab, from the barn into her bedroom.

Many of her stories were about rescuing Peter. Instead of having an older brother to protect her, my mother felt it was up to her to protect her older brother. Once, she saved him from drowning in the Trent Canal, the waterway that ran through Campbellford. My mother and Peter were with their good friends, Bill and Charlie Shaw. When they decided they would swim across the canal and back, the Shaw boys and my mother were able to battle the strong current but Peter soon started to flail. My mother helped him to a buoy in the middle of the canal and told him to hang on. She finished swimming to the opposite shore and on her way back collected Peter and towed him to safety.

My mother also liked to describe how she championed many of her friends, like Ona Mitchell, a shy girl who didn't easily participate in social activities. My mother frequently boasted that she was responsible for introducing Ona to Harry, Ona's husband of over sixty years. Later, when my mother was working at the Bell Telephone Company, she offered friendship and moral support to a new employee, Goldie Glenn, who was being shunned by the other women in the office.

Since many of the young men in Campbellford signed up to fight in the Second World War, dances were organized in the town hall to support the local regiments. Frank Clarke, one of my mother's childhood friends, was sent overseas as a Chaplain. The night before his departure he was anxious and didn't want to be alone, but as a religious man he wasn't comfortable with the atmosphere in the dance hall. It was a beautiful fall evening, so my mother led Frank outside and the pair danced on the sidewalk. She would sing me verses from "Stormy Weather" or "Shine on Harvest Moon" and I would imagine a handsome man in uniform and my mother in a red and white polka dot party dress dancing under a sky of twinkling stars.

"I was probably the last girl Frank danced with," my mother would emphasize. "He didn't come back from the war."

My mother went to work for the Bell Telephone Company as soon as she graduated from high school. Her first assignment was to collect overdue accounts. When money was owed for a legitimate reason, she would defend the customers and insist that they be treated leniently. She described how she would stand up to her boss when he wanted to take stronger action than she thought was appropriate, but was quick to add that when she thought an outstanding bill ought to be paid, she made sure that it was. Sometimes, that meant standing outside the local bar to intercept a delinquent customer before a promised payment was spent on alcohol.

It was a long time before I recognized the common theme in my mother's stories or questioned why she was always the heroine of her adventures. I still sometimes wonder if the other characters would have had a different version of the events. Reality is, after all, as much about perception as it is fact.

My mother worked in Campbellford until 1950 when she was transferred to Bell offices in other towns in southeastern Ontario. During that time, she lived in hotel rooms during the week and returned to her hometown on the weekends. She continued to work until she married my father in 1958 and moved to Winnipeg.

I never learned how my mother and my father met. She would sometimes say that she was in Winnipeg visiting friends and was introduced to my father at a party. When I asked who the friends were or how she knew them, she would change the subject. As I got older, I suspected there was probably another man involved or some sort of scandal, but if that was true my mother wouldn't admit it, even when I asked her directly.

During their courtship, my mother continued to live in Ontario while my father remained in Manitoba. They soon found that a long distance relationship wasn't easy. Letters sent through the post didn't offer the immediate gratification of emails and text messages, and telephone calls and air travel were expensive. At least twice, my father made a return trip on the Greyhound bus from Winnipeg to Campbellford, a ride that took more than twenty-four hours each way. I suspect that the anticipation of future bus marathons prompted my father to propose to my mother less than a year after their romance began. Neither my mother, at thirty-seven-years old, nor my father, a forty-one-year-old widower with a young son, saw the need for a long engagement. The wedding was scheduled for October, just two and a half months after my father presented her with a simple diamond solitaire.

My mother and grandmother drove to Toronto to shop for a wedding dress at Eaton's on Queen Street. My grandmother was a practical woman and encouraged my mother to consider an outfit that she could wear for other occasions but my mother had waited a long time to get married and was determined to look like a bride. She chose a traditional veil and an avant-garde ballerina length, silk organza dress with long sleeves and a fitted, lace bodice that was nipped in tightly at the waist.

The wedding was a small affair in Peterborough, Ontario officiated by Rev. Floyde, the former Anglican Minister in Campbellford and a close friend of the Winstanley family. My father's only guests were his sister, Evelyn, and his eight-year-old son, Neil. A reception was held in the church hall immediately following the ceremony. Helen Trimble was my mother's matron of honour and her husband, John, was pressed into service as my father's best man. The wedding date had been changed to accommodate John's hunting schedule, and in later years, my mother and father were never sure whether their anniversary was the seventh or thirteenth of the month.

After a two-week honeymoon in Jamaica, my mother moved into my father's house on an acreage just outside of Winnipeg. The adjustment to married life was difficult. My father's first wife had died when Neil was only four months old, and he and my father had been alone for several years. My mother had given up her career and her friends and moved to a new city to become a stay-at-home stepmother. To make matters worse, my father drove the family car to work. In those days, two-car families were rare; an additional car was considered an unnecessary expense and my mother was forced to sell her beloved turquoise and white 1955 Chrysler. Losing her automobile meant losing her freedom, and my mother was left feeling isolated and abandoned.

My parents had only been married a little over a year when my brother, Kevin, was born. Despite a difficult first pregnancy, my mother wanted a daughter so she quickly became pregnant again and I was born in June 1961. She had to cope with two young children in addition to Neil, all without the support of her family and friends.

In the summer of 1960, my parents moved to the house on Thatcher Drive, just ten minutes away from the University of Manitoba where my father worked. The biggest advantage of the new location was that my mother could drive my father to work and have the car for the rest of the day.

The neighbourhood filled with young families and a group of women met regularly for coffee in the morning and to play bridge one afternoon a week. My mother claimed that she had nothing in common with the other women and refused to join in either activity. After a while, the invitations stopped.

My mother also claimed that she didn't get along with my father's brother, Angus, and his sister, Evelyn, because she didn't drink and they did. She frequently told me that Angus' wife would offer her young children beer, an act that horrified my teetotal mother. In later years, my Aunt Evelyn told me that my mother alienated them – that she was always comparing the prairies to the virtues of the east and that she hated everything about Winnipeg. There was probably some truth in Evelyn's allegations but whatever the reason, those difficult relationships left my mother feeling estranged and even more alone.

Without friends or family, she filled time with chores and hobbies, satisfying a need that her work at the Bell used to provide. She would rearrange furniture and reorganize closets, cupboards and drawers; she ironed towels and sheets and my father's underwear. She was a gifted seamstress and spent hours turning yards of fabric into Christmas dresses, tailored suits or a pair of curtains for the kitchen. She never sat and read a book. She never sat and thought. She always had work to do.

My maternal grandfather had a stroke just before I was born. As soon as I was old enough to travel, my mother took Kevin and me to visit her parents. For the next four years, the three of us spent at least two months every summer in Campbellford. Our visits were an opportunity for my mother to help with my grandfather, who eventually had another stroke and was paralyzed on his left side. The trips also offered my mother a chance to escape from her life in Winnipeg, if only for a limited time. My father and Neil joined us once in Campbellford for a short vacation but other than that, they stayed in Winnipeg and fended for themselves.

Even as a young child, I could sense my mother's happiness when she was surrounded by her Campbellford family and honourary relatives. If *Uncle* Bill Normington didn't stop by my grandmother's house for tea and a chat, we dropped in to see *Cousin* Mary Johnson or *Aunt* Helen Wood. There was always someone willing to take Kevin and me to the five-and-dime store on Front Street where we would each be allowed to select a treat from the penny candy counter or, if we were especially lucky, a small toy.

The last summer we were in Campbellford, my grandmother was in the hospital in Peterborough, about half an hour away. She had broken her hip earlier in the spring and had been in the hospital ever since. My mother spent every afternoon with her and looked after my grandfather at home.

It became clear early in the summer that Grandma was not going to regain her health. She had been put in a full body cast and had gone on a starvation diet in protest. My mother cleaned out her family home and held a large yard sale with little help from her brother. "It was too difficult for Peter to deal with," my mother said. "He was always the soft one."

After Grandma died, Grandpa came to live with us in Winnipeg. The main floor of our house was remodelled to add a wheelchair accessible bathroom, and the den was converted into his bedroom. Although he couldn't talk, my grandfather could make some guttural sounds and we learned to communicate. When my mother was angry with me, I would run into his room and pull his wheelchair in front of me while he warded her off with his good arm.

One Saturday in late October 1971, Grandpa's breathing became laboured and he was taken to Deer Lodge Hospital where he suffered a stroke that left him unconscious. My mother stayed alone at the hospital all day Saturday and Sunday while my father took care of Kevin and me at home. Late Sunday evening my father joined my mother at my grandfather's side and Kevin and I went to my Aunt Evelyn's house.

My mother lost her father that night, but she also lost another connection to Campbellford and her old life as Mamie Winstanley.

Chipman called April 20th to say the cheque for $4000 he sent out in January (2003) was returned to him in July - why didn't he phone and tell me or drop a letter to ask why I returned it - I must ask him
Checked bank book and didn't receive all of my RRIF money in January 2003 - Chipman says I wrote a letter asking for $4000 - don't remember

Re Chipman
at first I didn't remember writing letter requesting $4000 then Liz reminded me about taking a sum from RRIF out each year - (I do faintly remember this and writing letter - don't think my letter was silly or pitiful as Chipman says) want copy of letter which he should have kept so I can show his boss - he claims he is trying to get "as he says" a lot of income tax back for me
Would like phoptostat copy of transactions made to me in his records since 1999 (can compare with bank book)

Apparently letter I wrote him was begging him to send $4000 because I needed it I want to see my writing in the note -

42 Thatcher Drive
Winnipeg
May 5/04

City of Winnipeg Yard Flooding Division

Dear Sir or Madam:

About a month ago I complained about water from the neighbour's swimming pool draining into my yard. Last year and every few years ~~before that~~ prior the same complaint was made.

~~They~~ The neighbours back of us have a swimming pool at one end of the yard. They empty their water into my yard. This year there seems no end to it. ~~It~~ There was water under the stones in the back sun porch early in the spring, it then went under the floor in the family room – from there it goes through the bathroom floor (very moist) and into the garage. I have a drain in the garage but it spreads out and reaches the basement wall which in turn gives me water in my rec room. The carpet and underlay get ~~wet~~ soaked and I have to use electric heaters to dry them out. Very dangerous.

Having all this water is a worry I don't need. I realize the children like the pool – and it isn't that I begrudge it – but when people have pools they should take into the neighbour's lawn.

Sorry this letter is so long and boring but I would appreciate it if you could put a stop to this water once and for all.

Yours truly,
Mamie Murray

# Chapter Three

**MY FATHER, JOHN** Robert Murray, was a gentle man, a kind man, but I was never as close to him as I was to my mother. It's hard to explain why, except that my mother needed me in a way that my father didn't. She needed to have as much of me to herself as she could. And that was something that I could give her. So I did.

My father didn't enjoy talking about his childhood. I had only the barest of knowledge about his early life. My grandfather, Angus, was a respected orthopedic surgeon but had a difficult and demanding personality. My grandmother, Olive Violet, had trained as a nurse. She committed suicide when my father was twenty years old – something I learned as an adult, not from my father but from my Aunt Evelyn.

The family lived in Norwood Flats, a well-kept middle class Winnipeg neighbourhood. Like my mother's brother, Peter, my father was sickly as a child but the only lasting testament to his rocky start in life was his eyesight. My father had no vision in one eye, and the fifty per cent vision in his other eye deteriorated as he aged. Several years before he died, he was legally blind but not completely without sight. He was so skilled at hiding his disability, I was never sure what he could see and what he couldn't. As a child, I often shut one eye and reduced my other eye to a slit to mimic his view of the world. My simulation yielded only a hint of his everyday struggle.

My father was almost forty-four years old when I was born in 1961. For a man of his generation, he was an active and involved parent. He often took Kevin and me swimming or skating, and when we were little, he would play with us on the floor, building houses with our red plastic bricks, or waltzing me around the kitchen as I balanced on his slippered feet. When I was older my father taught me how to play cribbage and the two of us spent many hours moving pegs around the cribbage board and calculating combinations of cards totalling fifteen.

When I was five or six, my father started a Sunday afternoon tradition of taking Kevin and me to the Montcalm Motor Hotel for hot chocolate and then reading to us in front of our fireplace. One of the books he read over a series of afternoons was *Greyfriars Bobby*, about a dog in nineteenth century Edinburgh who guarded the grave of his owner for fourteen years. The story frequently moved my father to tears. As an adult, I like to imagine that he was touched by the notion that even in death the master was remembered and loved.

There were little things that my father did for me that no one else would ever think to do. From the time I was sixteen years old until I moved out of the house at twenty-six, he made sure that I signed my driver's license renewal and then quietly mailed it in with a cheque. The first year I was married, it didn't occur to me to send in the paperwork and I drove for an entire year without a valid license. Long after my father had retired, he would get up on winter mornings to start my car and scrape frost from the windshield. Every year on my birthday, he would tell me that the day I was born was a beautiful, sunny day.

My father rarely disciplined me, nor was he involved in the daily decisions that affected my life. My mother made all of those areas her domain. When I wanted to do something like sleep over at a friend's house, start ballet lessons or buy a new sweater, I asked my mother. If my father did offer an opinion, she generally overrode him either overtly or covertly, as if she and I belonged to a private club with our own set of rules. It was only on rare occasions when my mother wanted to deny my request or felt that a reprimand was in order that she allowed me to think that my father wielded some authority.

"I'm sorry," she would then say. "It was your father's decision."

When I was a child, my relationship with my mother was intense and volatile but I always knew with absolute certainty that she loved me and would do anything for me. I was less sure about my father, perhaps because my mother had told me so often that he preferred boys to girls and that Neil was his favourite.

When my parents married, information about how to negotiate the sometimes problematic and perplexing dynamics of blended families was non-existent. As early as my fifth birthday, my mother had conscripted me into service as her confidante, especially when it concerned her feelings about Neil and what she saw as his rebellious teenage behaviour. She divulged her secrets in a hushed tone that made me feel privileged to be their recipient.

*He's out until all hours! He never tells us where he is! He does whatever he wants! He drinks too much!*

My mother's issues with Neil inevitably led to conflict between my parents. Their arguments consisted of heated discussions behind the closed door of the kitchen. I often perched on the stairway leading from the living room to the second floor, or crouched in a corner of the dining room, hoping to eavesdrop on their conversation. Shouting and name-calling wasn't my father's style, so more often than not, I could only catch an inaudible mumble but it didn't matter; my mother was quick to share her grievances with me.

*Your father never disciplines Neil! Your father doesn't listen to my concerns! Your father lets Neil run roughshod all over him!*

My mother eventually developed a bumpy red rash on her hands and forearms, claiming stress as the cause. A prescription for sleeping pills soon followed. One Sunday afternoon, after an in camera discussion with my father, my mother retreated to her bedroom with me in swift pursuit. I held my breath as I watched her swallow a couple of pills and crawl under the covers. My mother didn't believe in afternoon naps nor did she believe in taking medication unless it was absolutely necessary. I tiptoed into her room several times over the next couple of hours, watching her lie as motionless as Sleeping Beauty and worrying that she would never awaken. The incident compelled me to become my mother's protector as well as her sounding board.

The tension in the house eased when Neil left home in his late teens. The situation improved even more after he began dating Barb, whom my parents both agreed was a good influence on their son. With Barb as a buffer, my mother settled into a more comfortable relationship with Neil. After they were married, proximity and busy schedules limited their visits and everyone seemed to get along well.

Our family dynamic changed again after Sara was born. I was thrilled to be an auntie for the first time and I made a point of visiting Neil and Barb regularly to spend time with my little niece. Although my father didn't see baby Sara often, he was also happy with his new role as grandfather. My mother didn't share our enthusiasm. Sara's birth fuelled her insecurity about Neil's place in my father's affection and she resented the attention that Sara and Neil were receiving from both my father and me.

"You're wasting a lot of money on gas driving over there all the time," she told me.

In addition to her concern that Neil and Sara would usurp my father's love for her, she was also concerned that they could usurp my father's love for Kevin and me. Her anxiety only increased after Matthew was born almost three years later.

"You'd better watch out," she reminded me. "Your father has always liked boys better."

As I became older, I understood that my mother's comments had little to do with my father or Neil and more to do with her own insecurities. I also saw that in many ways my father treated Neil less favourably than either Kevin or me, mostly, I suspected, to avoid conflict with my mother. Those realizations made me more confident about my father's love for me.

My father wasn't overly demonstrative but he often called me Dearie or Daughter as a term of endearment. When I was backpacking in Europe after law school, or when he and my mother wintered in Florida, he wrote letters that always began with, "Dear Daughter." There was a time when I hated being addressed as Daughter; it made me feel as if my father had forgotten my name. As I became older, I recognized it for what it was – a special title that no one else could claim. I was my father's only daughter; more importantly, I was only his daughter. I was not his companion, confidante or protector as I was with my mother.

I only remember having two real arguments with my father and both of them involved my mother. When I was in Grade Twelve, my mother awoke on Mother's Day in excruciating pain but refused to go to the hospital until that evening. Her ruptured appendix went undiagnosed for several days, and if she hadn't been on intravenous antibiotics in the interim she might not have survived.

My father developed a routine of visiting my mother in the hospital after work and then stopping at the Montcalm Motor Hotel for a drink before coming home. At the time, my father's alcohol consumption was escalating, at least according to my mother. I was incensed that he was sitting in a bar when she was in the hospital, and even more so that he was drinking when he knew my mother didn't approve. One evening when he arrived home with beer on his breath, I told him loudly and angrily how I felt. I ended my rant by saying that I was ashamed of him.

"I never want you to feel ashamed of me," he said quietly. The next night he came home straight after his hospital visit.

A couple of years later, my mother and father were having a disagreement that ended with my mother getting in the car and driving away. I didn't know what they were arguing about but I assumed that my father was guilty and took it upon myself to defend my mother.

"How could you let her get in the car when she's upset?" I told him. "If she has an accident, it's all your fault."

By that time, my father was lying on the couch in the family room with one arm covering his eyes.

"You don't know what you're talking about," was his only response.

In the last several years of his life, my father rarely left the house without my mother. His declining health made it impossible for him to walk to the bus stop as he had in the past, and since he hadn't driven a car since the early 1980s, his options for independence were limited. My mother went to exercise classes, attended a ladies' group at the church, enjoyed an occasional lunch out with friends, and did various other activities and errands, all without my father. She was always careful not to leave him alone for too long – not because he couldn't be unattended but because she didn't want him to be lonely. As time passed, my mother became convinced that my father telephoned Neil every time she left the house and *talked for hours.*

"The minute I'm gone, he calls Neil. It never fails" she told me over and over.

Since Neil was not easily accessible by telephone during working hours it seemed unlikely that my father was spending much time talking to Neil during the day, let alone having substantial conversations on a regular basis. When I pointed out what I thought was an obvious weakness in my mother's theory, she remained undeterred.

"Those two have always had secrets from me," she protested. "I know what Neil and your father are up to."

My father's health had deteriorated further by the time our son was born on August 17, 1993. Davis Abraham John was named after Jeff's late father, Abraham, following the Jewish tradition to name babies after relatives who are no longer living, but Jeff and I agreed that it was also important to honour my father. He grinned when we told him his grandson's name.

Davis was a happy, healthy baby and for the first week of his life. I felt happy and healthy too. The day Jeff went back to work, I started to cry – not all the time, just if anyone asked me how I was coping with a new baby. My mother and father stopped by for a visit the second day I was home alone. I managed to hold off my tears until they were getting ready to leave.

My mother had an appointment to get her hair cut which she offered to cancel, but clearly wanted to keep.

"I'll stay here while you go," my father whispered to my mother. He turned to me and spoke in a louder voice.

"Mom will go. Your old Dad will stay here and look after Davis. You can have a nap. "

I was happy for my father to stay and keep me company but I was nervous about leaving him alone with Davis. My father's eyesight had always been poor but now chronic emphysema often made it difficult for him to breathe, and he was becoming progressively less steady on his feet. After my mother left, my father settled himself back on the couch. Davis was sleeping in a portable bassinet on the floor by his feet.

"Go on," my father said. "You go upstairs and have a nap. I'll be right here."

I looked at Davis, who was still sleeping soundly. I climbed the stairs to my bedroom with more than a little reluctance and lay on my bed, listening for the slightest noise that might indicate I was needed.

Forty-five minutes later I gave up the pretence of sleeping and crept back downstairs. My father was lying on his side on the floor beside the bassinet; Davis' left hand was curled around my father's right index finger. "We're okay here, Dearie," my father said without turning to look at me. "He's been a good little fella."

A few weeks after Davis was born, my father's health took a turn for the worse. What had been a steady but slow decline suddenly accelerated and became less predictable. There was no stroke or heart attack to explain the change, nor was there the diagnosis of a new disease that carried with it a dire prognosis. There was just a persistent deterioration of my father's ability to breathe; every intake of air took more and more effort and offered less and less strength. With every day that passed he became increasingly fragile, increasingly vulnerable.

By the end of November my father's weakened condition was severe enough that my mother was nervous about their annual four-month sojourn to Florida that was scheduled to begin immediately after Christmas.

"I can't tell your father I won't take him, Liz," my mother said. "Can you talk to him? Tell him you don't think we should go to Florida this year. Just don't let on that I put you up to it."

"I don't want to be the one to tell him he can't go to Florida, Mom," I protested.

"Okay, then, I guess we'll just have to go," she responded.

Eventually the thought of my mother being alone in Florida with my dying father was too much for me.

"Do you think a winter vacation is a good idea this year, Dad?" I asked tentatively.

"If I can, I want to go," my father said. "It will likely be the last time."

His answer broke my heart. I couldn't deny that what he said was true. Nor could I suggest that if he went, he might not make it home alive. My father was clearly contemplating the possibilities.

On the twenty-second of December, my father quietly cancelled the reservation for the condominium that my parents had rented for the last ten winters. He had tears in his eyes when he told my mother and me what he had done.

After my father resolved to stay in Winnipeg, the momentum of his decline slowed. By the time I returned to work the second week of January, my father's health had plateaued and he was able to manage with the assistance of inhalers and other medication. He was still frail, but he had a quality of life that he really did seem to enjoy. When the expected finally happened, we were all surprised.

The telephone rang at seven-thirty on the evening of Tuesday, the fifteenth of February. I was upstairs in Davis' room, rocking our almost six-month-old son and reading him nursery rhymes. Jeff appeared in the doorway wearing a concerned frown and holding the receiver in one hand.

"It's your mom," he said. "She sounds pretty bad."

She told me that my father had not had a good day. He was having a lot of trouble breathing and nothing seemed to help. She had tried to convince him to go to the hospital but he had refused. She sounded sad and afraid.

"Do you want me to come over?"

"Maybe see if Jeff will come," my mother replied. "Your father might go to the hospital for him."

There were always things that my mother thought a man could do better than a woman, but it occurred to me that by asking for Jeff, she was trying to shield me from what was really happening at her house.

"Okay," I said.

Protected by a bubble of warm baby, *Hey Diddle Diddle* and talcum powder, I felt guilty as soon as I spoke. I didn't want to go and do my duty as a daughter; I wanted to stay home and be a mother. I sent Jeff to help my mother while I stayed and put Davis to bed.

"Everything's okay here," Jeff said when he called about an hour and a half later. "Your Dad is in bed now and I'm sitting with your Mom. I'll be home soon."

The telephone rang just as I head the squeak of our side door announcing Jeff's return.

"Liz, I've called for an ambulance," my mother said.

"Jeff," I shouted, "You've got to go back!"

Before I hung up the receiver, he was gone again.

I waited for Jeff's sister, Esther, to come and watch Davis. By the time I arrived at my parents' house the ambulance was gone. My mother was sitting on the couch in the living room. She was fingering a soggy ball of tissue in one hand, and Jeff was holding the other. She looked exhausted. Her eyes were dull and unfocused – like the eyes of a soldier who had seen too many dead bodies too many times. When she finally stood up with her arms extended I wasn't sure if she was offering me a hug or asking for one for herself. My mother was usually more comfortable with a quick squeeze or a pat on the back but when we folded our arms around each other, she pulled me close and held me tightly against her. What I had known the moment I came in the house was suddenly real. My father was dead.

Later that night, when I had cried all the tears I was going to cry and we were back in our own house, Jeff told me what had happened. During the first visit, he had helped my father to his bed. My father had always liked Jeff. They shared a playful sense of humour, an even temper and a fondness for corned beef and rye bread.

"You're a good boy," my father had said softly. He called Jeff back as he was leaving the room. "No, I'm sorry. You're a man, not a boy. You'll take good care of Elizabeth and Davis."

By the time Jeff had returned to the house after my mother's second telephone call, the paramedics were trying to resuscitate my father on the floor in the living room.

There's something surreal about the death of a parent. I felt detached from the gravity of the news, as if I was a character in a novel. On the way to my mother's house the next morning, I looked at the people on the streets and in the cars around me. A well-dressed woman stood at the bus stop with her young child. A rumpled taxi driver was having an animated discussion with his passenger in the back seat. A man on a bicycle whizzed past me, the flap of his backpack blowing in the breeze. Their lives were proceeding just as they had the day before and the day before that. Our lives had changed forever.

My mother had always insisted that she was independent and self-sufficient. She liked to say that she *didn't need anyone* and would be *just fine* on her own.

I had always known that my mother's claims were more bravado than fact but that became increasingly obvious as soon as my father died. When we started to plan the funeral, my mother chose the hymns and then couldn't bear to do any more. I finalized my father's service in Winnipeg and arranged a second service when months later we buried his ashes in Campbellford.

In the days and weeks following my father's death, as my mother slowly came to terms with her loss, she turned to Jeff and me for support. Jeff and Davis and I also relied on her.

For five days a week, at precisely fifteen minutes past noon, I called my mother so that we could eat lunch together. I was at my desk at the office and she was at her kitchen table. Jeff handled all of the paperwork that needed to be done in connection with my father's estate and managed the maintenance on my mother's house. My mother looked after Davis one day a week while I was at work and on many occasions allowed him to sleep overnight. The four of us had dinner together, either at her home or ours, at least twice a week.

We were all settling into a rhythm, a pattern of life without my father. Then, just ten months after my father died, I was diagnosed with cancer, and everything changed again.

# Chapter Four

**IN EARLY DECEMBER** 1994, Jeff and I were celebrating Hanukkah with Dr. Les Garber and his family. Jeff's relationship with Les and his wife, Laura, stretched back to their elementary school days at Talmud Torah in the north end of Winnipeg. I met the couple shortly after Jeff and I started dating, and the four of us had been friends ever since. Their rambunctious household included a five year old, a two year old, a four-month-old baby, and a shaggy Golden Retriever with paws as large as dinner plates. The Garbers always made us feel welcome and as we sat around their kitchen table and passed platters of potato latkes and roast chicken, it felt wonderful to be in the company of friends, with no crises to attend to, no clients to serve or parent to console.

Les had recently completed his training as an Ear, Nose and Throat surgeon. A canker-like sore on my tongue that had been bothering me for several months was causing me some pain that evening, so after dinner, I jokingly asked Les what I could do. We all laughed when he pulled out a flashlight and instructed me to open my mouth.

After a quick prod of my tongue, he sat back in his chair in stony silence.

"What's wrong, Les?" I said, trying to tease him out of his reverie. "Am I going to die?"

He raised his eyes and stared at me without smiling.

"I have to treat you like any other patient," he muttered.

"Okay by me," I replied, still laughing.

Les prescribed an antibiotic ointment and told me to call him if the sore didn't heal within a week. I agreed, dutifully applied the ointment, and then continued to ignore the problem.

Over the past sixteen months, I had given birth to our son, returned to work after a reduced maternity leave to be co-counsel on a four month trial, lost my father, worried about my mother, and negotiated a change in my employment status from full-time lawyer to something less than full-time.

Within the space of five days, Jeff and I had sold our house, purchased a lot, and were in the process of discussing a building design with our contractor. Stress seemed like a reasonable explanation for the sore but Les had a different concern. At the end of the week, he called and firmly suggested that I come to the hospital the following day for a biopsy.

The next afternoon I sat in an examining room at the Ear, Nose, and Throat clinic at the Health Sciences Centre and watched Les assemble the tools he needed to remove small pieces of the sore on my tongue. Although I was nervous about having my tongue pierced by multiple needles, the outcome of the biopsy still didn't concern me.

After the procedure, Les looked at me with a half-smile. "You know," he said, "when I looked at your tongue the other night I was worried, but nine times out of ten I know if there's a problem as soon as I do the biopsy. I'm pretty sure now that everything's okay. Call me on Friday. I should have the results by then."

I didn't call Les on Friday. Christmas was nine days away and I was busy with errands and preparations for a gathering that Jeff and I were to attend that evening. There was another party on Saturday night and a holiday open house on Sunday afternoon. For the moment, I was focused on whether to buy Davis a Little Tikes truck or toddler-sized building blocks as a present from Santa. Les had already convinced me that I had no reason to feel anxious; the results of the biopsy didn't cross my mind.

We arrived home after the open house at six o'clock on Sunday evening. Davis had missed his afternoon nap and was over-stimulated from an afternoon of fun. I wedged him into his highchair and offered him a sippy cup with milk while I considered quick and easy dinner options.

Davis' bowl was still half full of Kraft Dinner when the doorbell rang. Jeff was standing by the stove holding a fork in one hand and the pot of bright orange noodles in the other. "I'll get it," he said hopefully, as if there was a chance that a perfectly cooked roast beef dinner might be waiting on the front step.

"Hey, how are you?"

I heard the surprise in Jeff's voice. A few muted words were spoken before I realized that our visitor was Les.

"How's my tongue?" I called from the kitchen after wiping a swath of cheesy sauce from Davis' chin. There was a moment of silence before he replied.

"Liz, we have a problem."

It took Les less than thirty seconds to confirm that I had cancer and instantly shatter my once easy confidence about our future. If I had found a lump in my breast, I might have suspected that it was cancer, but I had never heard of tongue cancer. Even if I had, as a non-smoking, non-drinking, thirty-three-year-old woman, I would never have considered myself to be at risk. The fact that I was totally oblivious to the disease didn't change the diagnosis. What followed was a flurry of appointments and tests. By Christmas, my surgical oncologist had determined that approximately one third of my tongue and all of the lymph nodes in the right side of my neck would be removed on Friday, January 13, 1995. We chose to believe that the date was a good omen.

The wait for my scheduled surgery was excruciating, allowing me plenty of opportunities to worry, which I did with increasing regularity. While a basic plan for the surgery had been established, there were many questions that could only be answered during or after the operation. Would it be possible to remove the necessary portion of my tongue without splitting my chin in half? Would I have to have a tracheotomy? How much pain would I experience? Would radiation or chemotherapy be needed as follow-up treatment? Would reconstruction of my tongue be necessary? Would I be able to speak intelligibly?

Reconstruction would require a portion of a muscle from my left wrist and an artery from my arm to be removed and attached in my mouth, and I dreaded the thought of the additional surgery. I was terrified that if that procedure was required, it meant the cancer was more advanced than we had contemplated.

I worried about all of those things but I worried more about Davis, Jeff, and my mother. It helped that Davis was too young to understand what was happening. Jeff was anxious but we spent a lot of time talking, crying and even laughing about our fears. My mother was exceptionally vulnerable and she concerned me the most. My father had not even been dead a year, and now she had to face the possibility of losing me as well. She wouldn't admit that she was frightened and steadfastly maintained that there was *no need to worry; everything would be just fine*. Her uneasy stoicism couldn't mask the tears in her eyes or the quiver in her voice whenever we were together.

Jeff and I decided that while I was in the hospital, Davis' home base would be my mother's house. He would go to his babysitter as usual on weekdays, which would give my mother the flexibility to keep her daily routine and to visit me. Jeff's sisters would provide respite on the weekend immediately following my surgery to allow my mother to come to the hospital. Our plan meant that Jeff would be free to be at my side as much as possible; Davis would be in a familiar environment at night and during the day, and my mother wouldn't be left completely alone. The arrangements provided me some comfort as the day of my surgery drew nearer.

Jeff and I arrived at the hospital at six o'clock in the morning of Friday the thirteenth. I was admitted and instructed to change into a hospital gown. My hand shook when I gave Jeff the bag with my clothes; he pressed his lips together to prevent himself from crying. In that moment my plight became very real. I had cancer. I was having an operation and we didn't really know what the outcome would be. While we waited for an orderly to take me to the surgical floor, a nurse came to insert an intravenous line in my wrist.

"Here, you give it a try," she said to a young man who was standing slightly behind her. The tag on his white coat told us that he was a paramedic-in-training.

"Oh, no! No tries today," I replied quickly. "You do it."

The nurse raised her eyebrows slightly but complied with my request with one quick jab. Jeff and I laughed guiltily at my refusal to be an intravenous guinea pig as we listened to the pair approach their next victim.

A few minutes later, the orderly appeared and I was wheeled away, with Jeff following as long as he was permitted. He squeezed my hand three times, our secret signal for "I love you", and then I was alone in a room full of stretchers, each with a patient waiting to be taken into an operating room. A man my age or younger on the stretcher next to mine winked at me and smiled invitingly, as if we had just been introduced at a cocktail party.

"What are you in for?" he asked.

"Cancer," I replied, and watched the smile fade from his face. If Jeff had been with me we would have enjoyed the dark humour. It wasn't as funny when I was alone.

My surgery lasted thirteen hours. Most of the minutes between Friday morning and Sunday morning were lost to me. When I first awoke on Saturday evening, my swollen tongue prevented me from speaking. I wrote Jeff a note. *Mom? Davis? Private room?* My last request of Jeff had been to ensure that I had a private room when I came out of surgery but I was glad that my first thoughts had been for my mother and my son. The second time I regained consciousness, it was just after eleven o'clock Saturday night. Jeff and his sister, Esther, were by my side. Then I was gone again.

Jeff and my mother arrived on Sunday morning as I was waiting to be taken from ICU to a step-down unit on a surgical ward. I had a feeding tube coming out of my nose and drainage tubes in my neck and my left arm, which was immobilized in a splint from my hand to my elbow. Reconstruction had been necessary. An intravenous line in my right arm connected me to a morphine pump. My mother's eyes widened and her bottom lip trembled as she stared at me.

"How are you feeling, Dear?"

She leaned close to my ear and spoke slowly in an extra loud voice that wavered on the dear. She never called me *Dear*. I glanced at Jeff and saw that he was thinking the same as I was. I couldn't talk but I could hear just fine. My mother looked as if she had spent the past two nights staring at her bedroom ceiling. Jeff didn't look much better.

It was only after I was home that I learned what had happened before Jeff and my mother came to the hospital that day. My mother had brought Davis to our house just after nine o'clock in the morning, where Jeff's sisters were waiting to take over babysitting duties. Jeff knew that my cheeks and jaw were swollen and bruised, and that my tongue was the size of a Big Mac. He was apprehensive that my mother would be upset by my condition and thought that it might be easier for all of us if she waited another day before she came to visit. My mother disagreed. I was her daughter and she wanted to see me.

Finally, my mother stormed out of the house, hopped in her car and sped away. Esther insisted that Jeff go after her and give in to her wishes. What followed was a "Thelma and Louise"-style, cross-city car chase that ended with reconciliation on the side of Bishop Grandin Boulevard, the closest thing to a freeway in the city of Winnipeg. I knew that Jeff's intentions had been good but I was grateful that he and my mother had mended their differences. I needed to know that my mother had survived the operation as much as she had needed to see that I was stable and recovering.

After that first Sunday, my mother wasn't a frequent or lengthy visitor. She came to the hospital regularly, usually in the early afternoon, but she didn't stay long. She would kiss my forehead and tell me in an artificially cheery voice that she could see that I was much better, and then she would fuss with the flowers and cards I had received. She found it difficult to sit and look at me, and when she did, she would have to work hard to keep her tears in check. As I slowly recuperated, I kept her busy buying magazines at the gift shop or walking me up and down the hospital hallways. When I had been in the hospital for almost a week, I asked her to help me wash and blow-dry my hair.

Private rooms at the Health Sciences Centre were in short supply, and the one Jeff managed to secure for me was located on the burn unit rather than the post-surgery ward. This meant that I had what we referred to as a "junior suite." As well as the bedroom, there was an antechamber fitted with a large sink on a long counter. To reduce the risk of susceptible burn patients being infected, visitors were expected to don sterile gowns and scrub any exposed skin as soon as they entered the room.

My mother wrestled a vinyl armchair in front of the sink and laid out our limited beauty supplies – shampoo, conditioner, brush and hairdryer. I arranged the tube that connected the IV stand to my hand and cautiously sat with a pillow and a rolled towel to support my neck. Although it was more of an ordeal than I had anticipated, we managed to wash my chin-length hair and rinse out most of the shampoo. Our efforts soaked the collar of the red and navy plaid pyjamas that I had worn for my first foray out of a blue hospital gown, but we considered that a minor misfortune. I wrapped my head in a towel turban and waited while my mother rinsed the sink. She gently removed the tangles from my wet hair before pointing the blow dryer at my head. The room was cool and my damp pyjama top made me shiver. The warm air from the dryer felt wonderful.

From the time I was in Grade Two until the middle of Grade Five when I had a short pixie cut, my mother had curled my hair every morning before I left for school. We shared the same fine hair, as soft and insubstantial as duck down; she believed that curls added body to my limp locks. I'm sure that's what she was thinking that day in the hospital when she selected an inch-wide strip of hair from above my ear and wound it around the brush until the bristles rested on my scalp. After directing a blast of air at her handiwork, she attempted to unwind the brush, hoping to see a fat, bouncy curl. The prickly bristles weren't eager to surrender and the more she pulled and twisted, the more entrenched the brush became.

My hair was half-soaked, my tongue was enlarged, my neck and face were swollen and bruised, and I was now sure that the side of my head had a large bald patch. I was frustrated with her failed effort, and she was becoming increasingly alarmed that she would tug too hard and hurt me. We both began to cry. I sat in the vinyl armchair with the hairbrush dangling from my ear.

My mother stood by my side with a firm hold on the blow drier. I knew that neither of us was really crying about the hairbrush.

I was discharged from the hospital late in the afternoon on day eleven. I hadn't seen my seventeenth-month-old son since the night before my surgery, and I was aching to hold him in my arms. Jeff and I decided to pick up Davis from his babysitter and deliver him to his grandmother.

As Jeff was strapping him into the car seat, Davis looked at me, and then turned his head and stared out the window. Despite my best attempts to get his attention, he kept his head turned for the duration of the fifteen minute drive. I was disturbed that he was angry with me but amused that he was so determined to show me how he was feeling. When we arrived at my mother's house, Davis ran to her and buried his head in her shoulder, with just a quick look back at me to make sure I was watching. I sat quietly on the floor and waited. After a minute or two, he pushed himself away from my mother and turned towards me. He flung himself onto my knee, hugging me hard around the neck. It hurt but it didn't matter. When Jeff and I left a short time later, Davis was sitting in his booster chair at the kitchen table, happily eating dinner with my mother.

Once I was home, I still had a lengthy recovery ahead of me. I was a hundred times better than I had been immediately after my surgery, but my left arm was still immobilized, my tongue, jaw and neck were still swollen, and I was still extremely tired. While my speech was intelligible, it was far from perfect. Davis spent the first several nights with my mother to allow me additional recovery time but even when he came home I couldn't lift him out of his crib when he called in the morning, fresh from sleep, wanting to be cuddled in my arms. The first time that Davis called for Jeff instead of me, I ignored the pain in my arm and retrieved my son, unwilling to lose any more time with him. I had already lost too much.

My outpatient recovery regime included regular physiotherapy and speech therapy sessions at the Health Sciences Centre. With my arm in a splint, I was unable to drive so my mother eagerly offered to be my chauffeur. Five days a week for three weeks, she drove me to the hospital, sat on a chair outside my therapy room, then drove me home again.

"I don't mind," she told me. "It reminds me of all of those years I drove you to piano lessons."

One day as we were driving to the hospital, my mother pronounced that I *looked just like I did when I was a little girl*. Her words reminded me of the popular optical illusion, where some viewers observe the profile of a beautiful young woman and others see the face of a haggard crone. I didn't have the heart to tell my mother that I would never again be a carefree little girl.

Almost one year after my cancer diagnosis, my mother decided that she wanted a new fur coat. Although the allure of fur was a mystery to me, I agreed to join her on a shopping expedition.

"Why don't you try one on, too?" she asked over and over.

I eventually relented and slipped on a black beaver with a grey fox collar. The coat felt so luxurious that I didn't want to take it off.

"I'll buy it for you," my mother offered. I refused, but just barely.

A couple of stores later, my mother found the coat she wanted – a silver-beige mink.

"I"ll only buy it if we go back and buy the fox for you," she said.

We drove home with the two fur coats lying on the back seat. My mother looked at our treasures and then smiled at me.

"You'll wear that coat forever."

I returned her smile. I realized then that the gift was more than just a fur coat to my mother. It was a way for her to assure herself that I wasn't going to die.


CANCER IS SNEAKY. Once it finds a home in your body, it makes itself comfortable and settles in for a long stay. Sometimes it can be persuaded to leave without too much fuss; other times, it refuses to be evicted, hiding for months or even years, until it again makes its presence known. I was always aware of the possibility that my cancer could return but after more than two years without incident, I was starting to feel more secure. Jeff and I decided that it was time to have another baby.

As soon as I became pregnant, my cancer reappeared. My massage therapist found an enlarged lymph node in the left side of my neck and, given my history, suggested that I ought to have it examined. I stood at the old wooden desk in her reception area, the phone shaking slightly in my hand as I dialled Les' number and asked if I could stop by on my way home. Les examined me at his kitchen table, as he had two years and nine months earlier, and then told me to come to the hospital the next day for a biopsy. Two days later, he made another house call. My cancer was back.

Being diagnosed with cancer is terrifying. Being diagnosed with a recurrence is a million times worse. As Les delivered the news, I remembered what one oncologist had told us the first time.

"Be aggressive. You only have one chance to save your life."

From the time I first learned that I had cancer, my goal had been to live until Davis' eighteenth birthday. I was panic-stricken that I had used my one chance and might not reach that goal.

We saw doctors, obtained second opinions, and developed a treatment plan just as we did before. This time, there was the complicating issue of my pregnancy, which would likely survive surgery, but would prevent radiation or chemotherapy until after the baby was born. We were told that without additional treatment immediately after surgery, the cancer might be difficult to control. For a few hours I harboured the thought that we ought to continue my pregnancy and that it would all work out. Neither Jeff nor my mother shared my view. In the end, I agreed. Davis, my beautiful boy, was four years old and he needed me. I loved him too much to jeopardize my chance of survival.

I was receiving excellent care in Winnipeg but I wasn't a typical candidate for tongue cancer. Jeff and I wondered if we should seek advice from a major cancer clinic outside of Canada in addition to our local specialists. Our surgical oncologist supported our decision.

On October 22, 1997, the lymph nodes in the left side of my neck were removed. Because the cancerous node had burst, allowing cancer cells to adhere to my sternocleidomastoid muscle in my neck, that muscle was also removed. In early November, Jeff and I flew to Houston, Texas, to consult with oncologists at MD Anderson Cancer Center, and on November twenty-first, we went to Rush Institute in Chicago for a similar consultation. Two days later we spoke to our radiation oncologist in Winnipeg, struggling to reconcile the different recommendations for treatment that we had received. At seven-thirty on a Friday evening we placed the call from a pay phone in the lobby of the Art Institute of Chicago. Well-dressed couples were wandering through the galleries, admiring the Renoirs and Miros and Warhols. All we could think about was cancer.

On November 26, I had the first of thirty-five radiation treatments at CancerCare Manitoba. On the first of December, I started chemotherapy, which would continue weekly for seven weeks. After chemotherapy and radiation ended, I would be on a regime of interferon and cis-retinoic acid for one year. It was all overwhelming. One morning, I sat in our family room and cried. I couldn't stand the thought that if my treatments weren't successful another woman could someday move into my home and be a wife to Jeff and a mother to Davis. I had never been good at sharing.

Soon after I started radiation, my mother asked if she could come and see what it was all about. I had banned Jeff from attending; he had dissolved into tears as soon as the technician had prepared me for my first session. I was sure that my mother would find the procedure equally difficult to watch but it was something she wanted to do and I didn't want to refuse.

Radiation treatments are extremely precise. The patient must be motionless to ensure that the rays hit the desired target. To prevent me from moving during my treatment, a clear plastic mould of my head and neck was placed over me and bolted to the table. The mask had holes for my mouth and nose but I had to fight the feeling that I was being suffocated. After a few seconds, the feeling would subside and I would be able to relax. The process was uncomfortable but not painful. By the time my mother came to watch, I knew the routine well. I tried to project a calm confidence as we walked into the treatment room. I lay on the table with my mother clutching my right hand so hard that her nails dug into my palm. A radiation technologist lowered the plastic mold while another waited to bolt it into place. My hand went slack.

"It's okay, I've got you," someone said. Out of the corner of my eye I saw one of the technologists lunge sideways. My mother was led out of the room. I wanted to get up to help her but the mould held me down.

"Don't worry, she's okay," the other technician told me.

Later, I found my mother sitting on a chair in the waiting area.

"I'm sorry, Liz," she said when she saw me.


Neither Jeff nor Davis nor I would have endured the nineteen months of treatment without the help of my mother. Davis stayed with her while I was in the hospital for surgery and when Jeff and I flew to Houston and Chicago. Monday was my chemotherapy day so Davis spent every Monday night at my mother's as well as many other nights when I wasn't feeling well or was just too tired to manage. She regularly went to watch Davis' swimming and skating lessons, and took him to Kindermusik classes most Tuesday afternoons. She drove Davis to nursery school every Monday, Wednesday, and Friday morning from October to the end of May, and took over my volunteer shifts as "helper mom." At the end of the school year, Davis' teacher told me that Davis and my mother shared the closest grandmother-grandchild relationship that she had ever seen. By the summer of 1998, I was so exhausted that I could barely function. My mother generously gave Davis all of the love and attention he needed to get through that stressful time unscathed.

At the time, I thought that my mother had dealt with my illness reasonably well. In retrospect, clues were being dropped like bread crumbs, waiting to lead me to the truth. The day after I told my mother about the cancer recurring, I asked her if she had spoken to her brother, Peter, who lived in Cambridge, Ontario. She told me she hadn't, but that she would do so on the weekend. That evening, my Uncle Peter called me to offer his support. He said that he and my Aunt Marion had told my mother the day before that they would come to Winnipeg immediately if they could be of assistance. My mother had no recollection of their conversation, even after I reminded her of what Peter had said.

When Jeff and I were preparing to leave for Houston, I assured my mother that her snow removal service was in place should it snow when we were out of town. I had been organizing the service since my father died in 1994, so this was the expected arrangement. After the first snowfall – which didn't occur until the first week of December – the company called me. When they had arrived at my mother's house, she had sent them away. She told them that she *always did her own snow and didn't need anyone else doing it for her.* They left as she instructed, but since they had been clearing her driveway for the past three winters, they wanted to know if they should go back.

Had I not been absorbed with my own ill health I might have been more concerned about my mother's memory lapses and unusual behaviour. Then again, it's possible that I might have assumed that her actions were nothing more than the normal aging of a sometimes difficult and determined woman. After all, I hadn't thought that the sore on my tongue was cancer, either.

# Chapter Five

JEFF ALWAYS TREATED my mother with a gentle forbearance. When she was difficult, he tried to tease or cajole her until she adopted a more reasonable approach. When she needed help, he was quick to offer his assistance. Right from the start he went out of his way to forge a special relationship with her.

Shortly after we were married, Jeff went to Toronto to visit his old friend, Joel. On a whim, they decided to make the two-and-a-half hour trek to Campbellford. When they arrived, Jeff called my mother's friend, Goldie, who agreed to act as their tour guide. Goldie was on the phone to my mother extolling Jeff's virtues as soon as he left town. For years after, Goldie told my mother how lucky she was to have him for a son-in-law. My mother's typical response was that Jeff was a good boy when he was sleeping but she preened whenever she repeated Goldie's comments.

After my mother moved to Winnipeg she continued to subscribe to *The Campbellford Herald* even though she often complained that it didn't contain any real news. Jeff was the one person who could get away with poking fun at the weekly newspaper without raising my mother's defences. He liked to spread the paper in front of him on the kitchen table while my mother busied herself with ironing, sewing or washing dishes. She would pretend to ignore him as he read fabricated headlines: "Cat Stuck in Tree – Fire Department Called." "Farmer's Cow Gives Birth To Two-Headed Calf." "Local Girl Wins Pie Eating Contest at Toronto Fair."

"Oh, Jeff, you're such an ass," she would finally say, struggling to preserve her stern expression.

At the family cottage, when everyone else was relaxing, my mother insisted on busying herself with make-work projects. Her movement came not just from desire, but from a visceral need, almost as if there was a demon locked in her psyche that she could only control with the force of her nervous energy.

It wasn't often that she could be convinced to set aside her work but Jeff did his best to encourage her to enjoy some leisure time. On one occasion, he challenged my mother to sit still for five minutes. She sat in a chair with one leg crossed over the other, her top foot swinging and her fingers tapping the rhythm of a song only she could hear. My mother's fidgeting increased and long before the time had expired she jumped to her feet and offered her standard response to Jeff's teasing.

"Oh Jeff, you're such an ass," she said with a smile.

Jeff was always ready to forgive my mother's foibles but even his patience was put to the test in the summer of 2000 at Falcon Lake.

My father had secured our lakefront lot in the early 1950s when the Government of Manitoba began offering long-term leases on properties in the Whiteshell Provincial Park. He cleared the land and built a flat roof structure with three small bedrooms and a galley kitchen. Modest improvements were slowly made over the next three decades. An indoor toilet and shower were installed and bedroom doors replaced bamboo curtains. In the early 1980s, a generous addition lengthened the living area and added a fourth bedroom. My mother and father did most of the work themselves so the end result was decidedly rustic.

Despite its limitations, the cottage had been a fixture of my childhood, and as an adult I cherished it as an escape from the pressures of everyday life. My mother's feelings were more complicated. She was sensitive because the cottage had been a part of my father's life with Neil that predated her arrival. She frequently claimed that Neil had asserted a proprietary interest in the cottage right from the start, meaning from the day she had married my father. My mother voiced her complaints even though Neil had moved out of the house and had stopped coming to the cottage with the rest of our family. I didn't understand the problem but I accepted my mother's opinion as fact.

Later, when Neil did start coming to Falcon Lake with Barb, he didn't seem to show a greater sense of entitlement, nor did he seem to resent sharing the cottage with the rest of the family. My mother thought differently.

"He still thinks this place is his," she said repeatedly.

After Sara and Matthew were born, Neil and Barb brought the children to stay for a weekend or two each summer. My mother grumbled even more.

"It's just too much work to have so many people in one cottage," she told Barb. "You need to get your own."


THE DAY OF the cottage altercation began like most Saturdays that July. The weather was fine and I rose early, happy to sit in the stillness of the morning, drinking a cup of tea and watching the sailboats across Falcon Lake set up for their first race. Jeff and Davis were still sleeping.

My mother sat in moody silence eating her breakfast in the kitchen. She had been irritable when she arrived late the night before so I felt vaguely uneasy as she pushed away from the table and walked slowly to the chair where I was sitting. She stopped and stared down at me.

"I've decided to sell the cottage."

I took another sip of tea. This wasn't the first time that my mother had threatened to sell. Since my father's death six years earlier, my mother had become increasingly determined to exercise control over her domain and the warning was one way of ensuring that we knew who was in charge. It wasn't that she didn't want us at the cottage; she did. The impasse was that she wanted us there completely on her terms.

I chose my words carefully. "Well, if you want to sell the cottage, maybe Jeff and I could buy it," I said.

Her lip curled slightly.

"You couldn't afford it."

"How do you know? I'm sure we could work something out."

My mother shook her head.

"No way. Besides, that wouldn't be fair to Kevin and Neil. How would they feel if I gave you the cottage."

She said this as a statement, rather than a question. I suspected my mother had deliberately misunderstood me.

"I'm not asking you to give me the cottage. I'm asking you to sell me the cottage if you're planning to sell it anyway. I'll talk to Kevin and Neil. They could approve whatever we decide."

"No way," my mother said again, slightly louder than before. "And I don't want you saying anything to them either. I'll decide when the cottage is sold, and who I sell it to. It's not up to any of you."

"You're not making any sense. If you want to sell the cottage, why can't you let Jeff and me buy it?"

My voice had also risen. My mother stood looking down at me, arms folded, jaw jutting forward.

"I'll never sell the cottage to you."

My mother had asserted her authority in other ways over the years. The summer that Davis turned three, we brought our old television and VCR to the cottage and set them up in a dark corner of the living room. Davis was curled up in an armchair, enthralled by a pre-Disney version of Peter Pan, when my mother arrived the next morning. She deposited her overnight bag on a chair; her eyes moved from Davis to the television and back again and her lips compressed into a thin line. The door slammed behind her as she returned to her car for another load. Jeff, who had just finished cutting the lawn, met her on the front step.

"What's that television set doing here?" my mother demanded.

"We brought it so Davis can watch movies," Jeff replied, oblivious to my mother's growing anger. He reached to take the cooler from her arms.

"Well it's my cottage and I don't want it here," my mother said, twisting her body to avoid Jeff's outstretched hands.

In subsequent summers we made sure that we asked my mother's permission before we tried to introduce any change but we soon learned that it didn't matter what we requested; my mother refused to modify the status quo in any way.

The rusty, twelve-year-old barbeque languished at the front of the cottage unused because she maintained that it worked fine. Our plea to replace the single beds in our bedroom with a double bed was denied on the basis that it wasn't necessary. Even the mattresses that provided little support for Jeff's bad back were all you needed at a cottage, in my mother's view. Our tentative suggestion that Davis might enjoy a small motorboat was also dismissed.

My mother's desire for everything to remain the same also generated controversy around everyday activities. If we decided to take Davis to the beach rather than swim off the dock, my mother was resentful. When Jeff and I politely refused my mother's offer to make waffles for breakfast, she became sullen.

I was often on tenterhooks, uncertain as to what my mother would find fault with next. I tried to justify her positions, rationalizing that she missed my father more at the cottage than when she was in the city. Still, her refusal to sell Jeff and me the cottage had been puzzling.

Later that morning, Jeff and I were returning from a bike ride just as my mother came around the corner of the cottage, wiping her hands on the seat of her pants.

"That pump isn't working," she said. "I thought you had the plumber look at it."

"We did. Last weekend."

I glanced sideways at Jeff and grimaced. My mother intercepted the look; her lips tightened and turned down slightly at the corners.

"Well it's not working now. I could hear it running all night."

She stood in front of us, blocking our path to the front door. Her body was stiff and her hands were clenched by her sides.

"Look, Mom, we never know whether we should call the plumber or not. If we don't, you're mad because we're not taking care of things. If we do, you're mad because we should fix it ourselves." I held my arms open to the sky, like a prophet waiting to receive divine inspiration. "We can't win."

"Oh, Elizabeth, I've never known you to worry about what I think you should do. You guys just do whatever you want."

My mother glared at me and then at Jeff.

Jeff had had enough.

"That's not true," he said. "We've wanted to buy a new bed for our room for years now and we haven't because you don't want us to."

"That's right. I don't want a double bed in that room." My mother smirked. "If you want a new bed so badly, get your own cottage."

Jeff stared at my mother without blinking. My mother looked down at her feet.

"Pack up our things," he said, without turning his head. "We're leaving."

I spent the rest of the weekend in the city wondering if my mother was lonely. At the same time, relief flooded over me every time Jeff repeated that he was done with the cottage. As much as I loved my Falcon Lake hideaway I was afraid that if we continued to butt heads, my mother's relationship with Jeff or me would be irreparably damaged.

When I wasn't able to reach my mother by telephone by Wednesday afternoon, I knew she was avoiding my calls. I found her at home in the kitchen by her sewing machine, seam ripper in hand, eyes resolutely focused on a length of black and white wool.

"When did you get home from the cottage?" I asked, dropping onto a chair at the kitchen table. "I've been trying to get you."

I counted twenty seconds before my mother deigned to reply.

"Oh, Elizabeth, what does it matter?" she said, her tone as sharp as the needle in her sewing machine. "I know what you think of me."

"What I think of you? What are you talking about?"

Her sewing machine was quiet but she didn't turn to look at me.

"You said I should give you the cottage and then you didn't want to see me down there anymore."

"What?" I said again. "That's not what I said at all. You said you were going to sell the cottage. I suggested that Jeff and I could buy it. I didn't say anything about you not coming down. Why would I?"

"I know what I heard, Elizabeth."

The whirr of the sewing machine started up again. For half an hour

I cajoled and then pleaded that my mother listen to reason. She never acknowledged that her interpretation of our conversation was flawed but she did eventually soften. For the first time since I arrived, her eyes met mine.

"Will you come to the lake this weekend, then?" she asked. It was clear that my mother was clinging to a grudge that would only be dislodged if Jeff and I agreed to return to Falcon Lake.

"I don't want the cottage to be an issue between us," I said repeatedly.

"Let things be the way they've always been," she implored. "I know who I'm going to leave the cottage to. Someday you'll be able to make all of the decisions yourself."

I told her as diplomatically as possible that we wouldn't be back in the near future.

IN THE SPRING of 2001, one of Jeff's friends told us that he was building a new cottage at Victoria Beach on the southeastern shore of Lake Winnipeg. He offered to sell us his old cottage when he was ready to move. At the time, properties at Victoria Beach sold quickly and primarily by word of mouth. If you didn't know someone who knew someone who was selling, you were out of luck. We bought the cottage in July for possession on June 1, 2002, paperwork to follow.

My excitement was mixed with guilt and a feeling that I was abandoning my mother, even though we hadn't been to Falcon Lake for the better part of two summers. I wanted to put off telling her about our purchase for as long as possible, so Jeff and I agreed that we would say nothing until closer to the possession date.

By January, we had started to accumulate the things we would need to set up our summer home. The small items like dishes, cutlery and a toaster were easy to store unobtrusively. The larger items were more problematic. When we bought living room furniture on sale in early February, Jeff thought that we should begin sharing our news with our immediate family. I was still reluctant.

"Don't you think your mother is going to wonder why we have a couch and loveseat stuffed into the office?" he asked.

"She won't notice. She never goes into the basement," I replied.

By the end of March, when we had a stove, a portable dishwasher and a washer and dryer in our garage, Jeff tried lobbying again.

"Don't you think your mother is going to ask why our garage is full of appliances?"

"Why would she do that?" I asked.

I knew the time was soon coming when I was going to have to tell my mother that we had a cottage of our own but I was still anxious to keep it quiet for as along as possible.

A couple of weeks later, my mother called me with an offer she thought I wouldn't be able to refuse.

"Liz," she began enthusiastically, "how would you and Jeff and Davis like to go on a cruise to Alaska with me at the end of June? My treat."

I was backed into a corner and I knew it.

"Uh, well, Mom, this June isn't that good for us."

"Why not?" I could hear the disappointment in my mother's voice. "I mean after Davis finishes school."

"It's not that. It's just that this year we're trying out a cottage at Victoria Beach. It's Jeff's friend's cottage – we're doing a kind of rent with an option to buy thing."

It was as close as I wanted to come to the truth.

"Oh." She took a shaky breath.

"I mean, we probably will buy it. We just want to make sure we like it." I stumbled over the words. "Maybe we could go at the end of the summer."

"No, no. That's okay. It sounds like you've made your plans for this summer."

My mother adopted the bright tone that she used when she didn't want to admit her feelings were hurt.

"You could come and visit us," I said.

"Why would I do that? I have my own cottage to go to."

I reissued my invitation for my mother to visit us at Victoria Beach several times in our subsequent exchanges. She always refused.

"Stop asking me, Elizabeth," she finally said. "I will never come to Victoria Beach."

CAA sent notice for renewal of car license, have to have a total Examination, appointment at Dr. Kalansky's office on August 5th at 1:30

Appointment with Kalansky Aug 5/1:30
I had received a card from CAA for exam for driver's license renewal - had eye test on the way in - went into her office, she talked about something? In that conversation she mentioned a number - asked me afterwards what the number was, said I didn't remember, she then sent me down the hall for a blood test - person said it was hard for her to draw my blood

On August 5 after receiving letter from CAA
I took it into Dr. Kalansky to have a total
exam for Drivers license - she examined my
eyes - sent me for a blood test - no exam
was really given. Oh yes, during our short
conversation she named a number and
asked after a short talk what was the
number she said - I couldn't remember -
it was after that she sent me for a blood test
- never mentioned I should go back to her
office - the next morning she called and asked
why I didn't come back to her office - (she
had other people waiting) so I went back
down that afternoon. I apologized for not
going back the day before and I asked if
it was necessary for me to come back
to her office and she said no

# Chapter Six

**MY MOTHER SAT** on a chair in our family room and cried slow, silent tears. She rarely cried without a good reason. Crying, in her view, was a weakness. She had called fifteen minutes earlier and asked if she could come over and discuss something with me. When she arrived at my front door I had no idea what was wrong but my heart beat a little faster and I had an odd fluttering feeling in my stomach.

Since I had completed my cancer treatment five years earlier, I had unconsciously internalized a conviction that bad things happened when they were least expected. As I sat on the arm of my mother's chair and leaned in to give her a hug, I struggled to control my panic. She smelled like Oil of Olay, the face cream that she had used since I was a little girl.

"Mom, what is it?"

"I'm so tired. I haven't been sleeping lately." She rubbed her eyes, one hand for each eye. "Those neighbours are driving me crazy. I just can't take it anymore."

I started to feel less worried. My mother often had grievances against her neighbours. In the last few years her usual target was the family who lived behind her. She frequently complained that they were emptying the water from their above-ground pool into her backyard.

"The neighbours? You mean the swimming pool neighbours?"

"No, not them. The people who moved into the Ross's house next door." My mother's voice rose as she continued. "Those people cut the lower branches off the three pine trees on the side of the driveway. You know, the ones between my house and theirs."

When I was in Grade Five, I had brought the trees home as seedlings from a field trip to a reforestation reserve. The trees had been a tempestuous issue for my mother ever since my father first planted them beside the driveway. She said the seedlings would never amount to much and she wanted *real trees* planted to give privacy from the neighbours. More than thirty years later, each one was taller than the house, with wide, sweeping branches that overhung the driveway.

"Why would your neighbours do that?" I asked, raising my eyebrows.

I knew my mother was liable to omit key details in her complaints, particularly if those details shed an unfavourable light on her actions. Three years before, my mother had told Jeff that the contractor she had hired to replace the shingles on her roof had not been to work for two weeks and was not returning her telephone calls. She thought he wasn't talking to her because she was a woman. When Jeff spoke to the man, he learned that my mother had told the contractor that his work was unsatisfactory and she would be hiring someone else to finish the job. I was inclined to think there was more to the tree story than my mother was admitting.

"Did they talk to you about it? Were the branches covering part of their driveway?"

"No, they didn't talk to me about it." She emphasized each word as if my question was preposterous. "They just went right ahead and did it."

"Okaay." I drew out the word. "How do you know *they* cut the branches? Did you see them?"

"Of course I didn't see them!" she answered sharply. "Don't you think I would have stopped them if I saw them?" She paused. "But who else would cut those branches? I want Jeff to sue them for me."

Jeff was a lawyer with an old and established law firm in the city. He was extremely accommodating when it came to my mother, but he would never initiate legal action against my mother's neighbours based on the information she had provided.

"Well, Mom," I hedged, "you can't just sue your neighbours. You have to talk to them first. Find out what's what."

"I don't want to talk to them. I want to sue them." My mother's look reminded me of my son's pre-temper tantrum expression. "Why can't Jeff sue them for me?"

"You have to talk to them first," I reiterated. "They're your neighbours.

You have to live beside them." I rubbed my forehead. "Do you want me to talk to them for you?"

"No. If Jeff won't sue them, I'll have to think of something else."

She stood up and moved towards the door. For the moment, our discussion about the missing branches was over.

A few days later, I made an early morning trip to my mother's house to revisit the issue. I found her in the kitchen washing her breakfast dishes. I watched as she purposefully wiped a bowl with a soapy dishcloth, keeping her eyes focused on her task. A stack of old newspapers sat at one end of the kitchen table beside a loose pile of miscellaneous correspondence and junk mail. Three pairs of pants, a skirt and two blouses all in varying states of repair, were piled on her sewing machine. Scrawled reminder notes and newspaper clippings were taped to the refrigerator and a few cupboard doors. *Garbage day is Thursday. Manitoba Flood Forecast Revised Upwards.*

"Neil's coming over soon," my mother said, glancing sideways at me before quickly turning back to her dishes. "He's going to talk to the neighbours for me, since you won't do it."

My mother resorted to Neil whenever I didn't agree with something that she wanted done. "I guess I'll have to call Neil," she would say in a further attempt to have me accede to her wishes.

I took a breath and told her that my brother had phoned me and we had agreed that I would come instead.

"What do you mean?" she asked, turning to look at me, holding her soapy glove-covered hands in front of her, like a surgeon, scrubbed and ready for the operating room.

"He explained your crazy plan."

The creases in her forehead deepened as my mother narrowed her eyes. She opened her mouth to speak. I held up my hand.

"He said you told him that you would go out, and he was supposed to walk around outside until the neighbours appeared and asked him what he was doing."

I stared at my mother's face, hoping to maintain eye contact with her but she turned back to the sink.

"Then he was supposed to somehow point out that your trees were ruined because of how the branches had been cut. But he wasn't supposed to say who he was."

"That's not true," my mother said. There was a momentary pause in her movements before she retrieved a coffee mug from the water and began wiping it vigorously. "I told him the trouble I was having with the neighbours and he offered to come over and take pictures of the trees for me."

"He tells it a bit differently," I countered.

My mother turned to face me again. "You never believe me. You're never on my side." She deliberately freed each of her fingers from their rubber casing and threw her gloves into the sink. "And why did he tell *you*, anyway?"

"You told him I wouldn't help you, and he wanted to know why," I explained.

"You kids are all the same. You never stick by me. Not one of you."

She stood with her arms crossed. I got out of my chair intending to give her a hug but she waved me away.

"I said I *would* help you. Remember, you were sitting in my family room – "

"You told me you wouldn't help."

Her voice rose as she enunciated each word. She folded her arms across her chest and stared at me with cold eyes.

"No, I said Jeff wouldn't sue, but–"

"Elizabeth, it certainly *is* what you said." My mother only used my full name when she wanted to ensure that I knew she was angry with me.

"Mom, just listen to me. I told you it didn't make sense to start a court action against your neighbours without trying to talk to them first." I tried a conciliatory smile. "But I told you I would speak to your neighbours for you if you didn't want to."

She shook her head. Her mouth was a tight line.

"That's the first I've heard that. I might as well just give them my land, that's what they want anyway."

She turned and walked into the living room.

It was my turn to shake my head. I waited for a minute or two before I followed her to the front room. She was sitting in her favourite spot, one of the gold brocade wing chairs that flanked the brick fireplace. I sat on the couch opposite her chair, trying to control my increasing exasperation. When I sat down, she turned and looked out the front window.

"Mom, what are you talking about?"

"Just what I said. They want my land. I own that piece of land between our driveways, not them. But I might as well just let them have it."

There was a strip of grass approximately eight feet wide between her driveway and the driveway of the house next door. The denuded trees were on that strip of grass.

"Why do you think they want your land? Is it just the trees?"

"No, it's not *just* the trees." She scrunched her face and spoke in a mocking tone, as though I was slow to understand the situation. "Haven't you noticed their cement pots? They've put their cement pots right on my land."

She stood up and pointed out the window toward the offending neighbours.

I moved beside her. There were three large flowerpots behind my mother's trees, right beside the neighbour's driveway. I assumed that the pots had needed to be moved from their front step, which was under reconstruction.

"Okay –" I was having a hard time believing she was serious about this.

"Just forget it; you wouldn't understand." She turned her face away from me again. "And they keep on cutting that grass. It's my land. I can cut my own grass."

"Look, I told you I would talk to them for you. Do you want me to talk to them for you?"

"Just forget it," she repeated. She sat with one leg crossed over the other. The foot on her top leg moved up and down rapidly. "I'll just have to get a lawyer and deal with it myself."

Three more days passed. I had just finished my run on the treadmill and was retrieving my telephone messages. There were two. Both were from my mother.

In the first, she said that a sound outside had awakened her in the night. When she looked out her bedroom window, she noticed that someone had cut a branch from the tree on her front lawn farthest from her offending neighbours. She said that she had stayed up the rest of the night watching, in case the perpetrators returned. She just thought maybe I should know what was going on. And maybe I should come over.

As I listened, I could feel my neck and shoulder muscles tighten.

In the second message, my mother said that since she hadn't heard back from me, she had called the police. They would be right over. Maybe I should come too.

My mother was watching for intruders from her bedroom window when I arrived. She came downstairs and took up her watch in the living room. The heavy gold drapes that covered the window were open, but the sheer liners gave her some protection as she positioned herself so that she could see but not be seen. She stood and peered out the window as she repeated the information she had provided earlier, gesturing toward the tree now at issue.

I studied my mother as she spoke. The hair on one side of her head was flattened against her skull; on the other it was tousled and unkempt. She was wearing blue corduroy pants with her flannel pyjama top. Both of her slippers were pink but they were not a matched pair. I would have known that she had been up all night even if she hadn't told me.

"Have you eaten today, Mom?" I asked brightly. Food was often an afterthought for my mother.

"I think I had a piece of toast earlier. I can't remember."

Her eyes didn't leave the front yard.

"Let's have a cup of tea. And how about a bowl of soup or something?"

My mother followed me into the kitchen. Her place at the table was untouched. Each night before she went to bed, she set the table for breakfast the next day. As I filled the kettle with water, I noticed two pieces of bread standing in the toaster. I pressed the lever and watched the bread disappear.

"I don't know what I'm going to do," she said as she sat down. "I guess I'm just going to have to give them what they want." She tried to look defiant, but she just looked weary.

"So you think it was your neighbours who cut the tree last night? The same people who cut the other trees?"

"Well, of course, Elizabeth. Who else would cut my tree?"

My mother took a bite of toast, chewing slowly. Her eyes were glassy.

"Look, Mom, do you want me to go talk to them for you? Right now?"

"I think you'd better," she said. "I just don't know what else to do."

Her hand shook slightly as she held a finger of toast midway between her plate and her mouth. She set the toast on her plate and rested her head on the heel of her right hand.

"Do you think it's silly that I'm afraid to talk to them myself?"

She sounded uncertain, like a little girl who was reluctant to look under her bed in case there were monsters hiding there.

I paused for a fraction of a second. "It's perfectly understandable, Mom."

I covered her left hand with my right hand and gave a gentle squeeze. "Don't worry. I'll take care of it."

A woman with curly brown hair answered the neighbour's door. Her rectangular black wire glasses were fashionable but not trendy, and when she smiled I noticed a slight gap between her two front teeth. I liked what I saw. She didn't appear to be a woman who would knowingly terrorize her eighty-three-year-old neighbour.

"Hi there," I began. "My name is Liz Murray. My mother lives next door."

That pretty much exhausted what I knew I was going to say. The woman nodded once and smiled again, waiting for me to continue.

"I'm sorry; I don't know your name. My mother couldn't remember."

"Debbie Good," the woman replied. "Is there something I can help you with?"

Her tone was pleasant. She tilted her head and looked at me expectantly.

"Well, yes, I think there is. My mother is upset about the trees."

I pointed to the strip of land between the two houses. Debbie's eyebrows drew together, creasing her forehead and pushing her glasses down her nose.

"What do you mean?"

"My mother is upset that you pruned her trees without speaking to her," I continued, silently congratulating myself for my diplomacy.

Debbie shook her head and frowned.

"We didn't prune her trees. Mamie had that done last fall," she said, pronouncing my mother's name Me-me.

I stared at her. For a moment I couldn't think of anything to say.

"Are you sure?" I managed eventually.

"Yeah, she had some guys come last fall. She stood and told them which branches to cut and how to cut them."

That certainly sounded like my mother.

"My husband and I were outside doing our own yard work. To tell you the truth, it was kind of funny. Your mother directed the whole operation. The guys were looking a little frustrated."

That definitely sounded like my mother.

"Look, I'm really sorry," I said. "I guess she forgot."

My apology seemed inadequate, but Debbie smiled. I thought I should say something more, but I didn't know what.

"We're getting used to Mamie. She's an interesting neighbour. Sometimes—"

Debbie stopped speaking and motioned in the direction of my mother's house with her chin. I turned to look. My mother was walking slowly towards us. She had pulled on an old cardigan over her pyjama top but she was still wearing her mismatched slippers. She hadn't brushed her hair. Her arms were folded across her chest as if she was hugging herself.

"Oh, no," I said. I squeezed my eyes shut for a second.

"Don't worry." Debbie gave me a sympathetic half-smile. "I have an older mother too."

She started down her front steps and I followed close behind. We met my mother at the edge of the driveway. Debbie gave my mother a quick hug. My mother's body stiffened and then relaxed. After her initial discomfort, she didn't seem to mind Debbie's overture.

"Mamie, your daughter tells me that you think I trimmed the branches on those trees. I didn't, Mamie. I wouldn't do anything like that without asking you first."

My mother's eyes darted towards me before focusing on her neighbour. She touched Debbie's arm. Her movement was tentative.

"I didn't really think you would," she said, with a slight emphasis on the I. "You're such a nice person." She paused. "But Mike Zwarich from across the street told me he saw you cutting the branches," my mother continued. "He wanted to know if I had given you permission."

This version of the story was new but not surprising. When my father was alive she would use him as her fall guy; now she blamed poor Mike Zwarich.

Debbie shrugged slowly.

"I don't know why he would say that."

Her voice was gentle and she kept her eyes on my mother's face as she spoke.

The three of us stood in silence. I coughed and my mother glared at me and shook her head almost imperceptibly. The reproach was unnecessary. I had no intention of saying anything at this juncture.

"Well, now we know it wasn't you, who did trim those branches?" my mother asked.

She stood straighter now and her voice was stronger. She was ready to develop a new conspiracy theory, preferably with Debbie's assistance.

"Last fall my husband and I saw some men working around those trees," Debbie offered. "But I can't remember the name on their truck."

My mother's head dropped slightly, like a turtle pulling its head into its shell. She shook her head.

"That's strange. I didn't hire anyone," she finally said. "It must be the same person who cut those branches last night."

I couldn't tell if she still didn't remember or if she was bluffing. Debbie turned to me with a hint of a frown.

"She thinks someone cut a branch off that tree during the night," I said, pointing to the tree on the opposite side of my mother's property. Debbie looked incredulous and amused.

"I don't *think* someone cut a branch, I *know* it," my mother corrected.

I was considering the easiest way to extricate my mother when Debbie nudged my arm and nodded her head towards the road. A black and white police car was just pulling into my mother's driveway.

"Great." I thought. "This is just great."

My mother moved determinedly towards the police officer, shoulders back, arms swinging by her side, the last trace of her uncertainty gone.

The police officer introduced himself as Sergeant Dennison.

"Did one of you ladies make a complaint this morning?"

My mother responded affirmatively. She nodded and smiled while Sergeant Dennison verified her name and address and recorded the information in a small, black notebook. The officer looked at me.

"And do you live here as well?"

"Oh, no," I said, wanting to tell him that I wasn't buying into my mother's story. "This is my mother, but I have my own house. I don't live here."

"Now, the complaint we received was something about a tree."

"That's right, Officer," my mother began.

She told him how she had heard a loud, cracking noise in the night and got out of bed to see what was going on. She said at first she thought it was a car door slamming but when she looked out her bedroom window, she had noticed that a large branch was missing from one of her trees. She figured the cracking sound must have been the branch being cut from the trunk.

I watched Sergeant Dennison as he continued to record information in his notebook. His face was impassive as he listened to my mother's story. His questions were polite and courteous.

My mother continued. She admitted that, no, she hadn't seen anyone near the tree nor had she seen the missing branch anywhere around the tree. She said it was odd that whoever had cut the branch was able to get away so quickly but she'd been thinking about it and decided that there had to be more than one person involved. They probably had some kind of truck to cart the branch away. She thought they must have had it planned in advance. She told Sergeant Dennison that she spent the rest of the night watching out her bedroom window in case they returned. When it started to rain, she went out and covered the severed limb to preserve the evidence.

Sergeant Dennison looked at me. I opened my eyes wide and shrugged, hoping he would understand my message.

My mother started across the lawn.

"Come, I'll show you," she said.

Sergeant Dennison hesitated a moment, then followed behind her. I followed too. The grass was wet and the long blades were sharp against my sandaled feet. Sergeant Dennison's shoes left deep impressions that marked his path to the tree where my mother was now standing. The officer was not a large man – five foot nine at best, with a slight build – but in contrast to my mother, he looked substantial. I noticed how fragile she had become when I saw her standing in her pyjamas and slippers beside the policeman.

"See here." My mother pointed to a white plastic bag near the base of the tree. "I tied this around the branch so it wouldn't get wet. I wanted to make sure the cut marks weren't washed away."

She bent down and removed the bag from a greyed stump that had once been a major branch extending from the main tree trunk. There were no fresh wood shavings or chips to suggest a recent pruning. Nor were there any leaves, twigs or branches on the lawn in the near vicinity.

"Ma'am, if someone cut this tree in the middle of the night, he did a pretty good job." He gestured towards the ground. "And he cleaned up after himself really well, too. We don't get many cases where vandals clean up after themselves." He hesitated. "We really haven't had any cases of this kind of damage to trees, either."

I appreciated his tact but my mother didn't seem to understand.

"I know," she said. "It's strange. That's why I thought I should call you. Someone must have done it to get back at me, or to upset me or something."

"Well, I've taken the report. We'll be on the lookout for any vandals in the area."

He put his notebook and pen in his shirt pocket.

My mother wasn't ready to let him go. "Will you be interviewing any of my neighbours?" she asked. "Just in case someone else saw something I didn't."

"Not right now. Unless you can give me a good reason to, I don't think it's necessary at this point. We'll just keep a general lookout."

It was time for me to intervene. My mother could probably come up with a number of suspects for him to consider, including Debbie Good.

"No, no. We certainly appreciate your help," I said. "We'll leave it with you for now."


ALL WAS QUIET on the tree front until two weeks later when I retrieved a cheerful phone message from my mother.

"Liz, I've got a gentleman here I'd like you to meet. Can you come over right away, please?"

She had left the message at ten-thirty in the morning and it was now eleven o'clock. I briefly considered whether I ought to return her call.

She answered the phone halfway through the second ring.

"Oh, Liz," she said, even before I had said hello, "I'd like you to come over right away if you can. I have someone here I want you to meet."

She coyly refused to tell me the name of her guest or answer any of my questions.

"Just come over and see for yourself," she said.

I explained that I would have to have a quick shower and it would be forty-five minutes before I could get to her house.

"Get here as soon as you can. We'll be waiting."

When I arrived, there was a white pickup truck in the driveway with Kackenhoff Nursery painted in black letters on the back window. I entered the house without knocking and saw an older man in navy coveralls sitting in the wing chair on the left side of the fireplace. The man was tall and broad and had a grey crew cut. He filled the chair so completely it looked as if it had been made for a child. My mother was sitting in the matching chair on the right side of the fireplace. Her legs were crossed at her ankles and her hands rested in her lap. She inclined her head and smiled when she saw me.

"Come sit down. I want you to meet a friend of mine, Mr. Kackenhoff."

Mr. Kackenhoff looked uncomfortable. He tried to stand, and then remembered that he was balancing a china cup and saucer on his knee. Instead of rising, he made do with a nod.

I nodded back and turned to my mother.

"What's up?" I asked.

"Mr. Kackenhoff, here, was just telling me that those pine trees are ruined, and we ought to sue," she said. "But I'll let him tell you himself."

She crossed her arms and looked at the man sitting across from her.

"Well," he said, shifting his weight from side to side, "your mother says that her neighbours trimmed those pine trees beside her driveway without her permission. They didn't do a very good job, I don't think." He shifted his weight again. "I understand your husband's a lawyer. So maybe he could do something about it."

His voice trailed off. He shifted some more.

My eyes moved from Mr. Kackenhoff to my mother. Her gaze was challenging. She reached for the teacup on the end table beside her and smirked ever so slightly.

"Well, sir," I said sharply, still looking at my mother, "if it was the neighbours who trimmed the trees – and we don't know for sure that it was – I think it would be better to talk to them first, don't you?" I turned my head towards Mr. Kackenhoff as I finished my question.

The man's eyes were wide, his forehead furrowed. He put his teacup and saucer down and inched awkwardly toward the edge of his chair.

"Can I get you another cup of tea?" My mother wasn't willing to let him go that easily. "No need to rush off."

I looked at my watch. My mother had kept the poor man hostage in her living room for almost two hours.

Mr. Kackenhoff politely refused additional refreshment and made his way to the front door with my mother in close pursuit. She stood on the front step and waved as he walked to his truck.

"Isn't he a nice man?" she asked when she came back inside. "When he saw those trees he said he just had to talk to you about them. Well, maybe not you specifically, but he thought someone should do something. And then when I told him that Jeff was a lawyer, well, right away he offered to talk to him. I didn't want to bother Jeff at work, so I called you."

The farther she got into her story, the faster she spoke.

"He thinks we should take pictures of the trees so we have proof if we have to go to court."

She finished with a self-satisfied smile.

I stared at my mother and shook my head slightly. What could I say? The whole thing was beyond absurd.

# Chapter Seven

"HERE, LIZ, THIS is what I want you to look at. I get payments from two RRIF accounts at the beginning of every year, usually around the middle of January."

My mother and I were sitting at her kitchen table. She was holding her bankbook and three more were fanned out on the table in front of her.

"So what's the problem?" I asked.

"Well, that's what I can't puzzle out," she said. She closed the second bankbook and opened a third. Her hands shook slightly as she continued to shuffle the books back and forth. "I just don't understand this. I got a letter in the mail that said I missed one of my payments and they weren't going to give me the money." She scratched her head. "So I'm trying to figure out which payment I missed. I need to know why they won't give me my money."

"Let me have a look."

I took the books from her and looked for the payments for 2002, 2003, and 2004.

"They're all here, Mom, look." I reviewed the entries with her. "Can you show me the letter and I'll see what it says?"

"Well, I just told you what the letter said," she answered irritably.

My thoughts wandered as I watched her rifle through the pile of papers at the end of the brown Formica-topped table that my parents had purchased when they moved into their house in 1960. When I was in elementary school, my mother and I ate lunch together at that table five days a week. My mother believed that a table should always be set properly with placemats and bread and butter plates. I loved those lunches with my mother. Since Kevin didn't attend the neighbourhood school, I was guaranteed to have her for ninety minutes all to myself. In the winter, she would present me with a mug of hot chocolate that I would sip as she finished heating the soup or melted Velveeta cheese under the broiler. While we ate, my mother would tell me stories about the adventures she had growing up in Ontario or we would share copies of

*The People's Friend*, a women's magazine from Scotland that contained serial stories that we both enjoyed. The magazine was supposed to arrive weekly but more often two or three would come at once and my mother and I would pass the magazines back and forth so that we could read our favourite sagas in their proper sequence.

Spending time with my mother had once been one of my greatest pleasures.

"I know I had the letter right here but it's not here now," she lamented. "Oh, wait, wait, here it is!" She plucked a sheet of paper from the debris and handed me the letter from her investment advisor.

She had requested a capital payment from one of her Registered Retirement Income Fund accounts but hadn't cashed the issued cheque. After six months, the cheque had been cancelled and the funds had been deposited back into her account. My mother wasn't actually missing funds. The letter was simply to inform her about what had transpired.

A year ago, I had suggested that my mother obtain advice from an accountant to determine if she should be making capital withdrawals on an annual basis and if so, in what amounts. Apparently, she had gone ahead without a professional's input.

I bit my tongue and explained my understanding of the letter.

"If you want me to talk to this guy to make sure," – I glanced at the signature – "Art Chipman, I will."

Now my mother looked confused. "I don't remember asking for a capital payment." She pursed her lips and scrunched her forehead. "But he did say something about me writing a letter and begging for money." Her voice was indignant now. "Maybe you should talk to him, then. Call him now and I'll get on the other line."

"That's not going to work," I said, worried about what he may say to me. "I'll talk to him on my own." I looked at my watch. "I don't have time to call now, anyway. Let me take the letter and I'll call later this afternoon or tomorrow."

"No way. I want to hear what you're going to say." My mother was adamant in her demand to be privy to the conversation. I was equally adamant.

"Okay, then, just forget it," she said. "I'll deal with it myself."

Two hours later, I was at home unpacking groceries when the doorbell rang. My mother stood on the front step.

"Liz, I've changed my mind. You can call Mr. Chipman on your own. I don't need to listen."

She put her hand in the pocket of her windbreaker and pulled out the letter.

"Okay, I'll call him tomorrow morning." I was careful not to give her an opening to initiate further discussion about the problem. "Do you want to come in for a while?" I opened the door wider in support of my invitation. "Davis will be home from school soon."

"No thanks dear, not this time. I haven't gotten any work done today. I'll see Davis soon. Give him my love."

My mother rarely refused an opportunity to see my son. From the moment I shared the news with her that I was carrying a boy, she maintained that Davis was her baby as much as he was mine.

As our son grew from an infant to a toddler to a preschooler, her devotion to him increased. My mother's house was quickly transformed into Davis' second residence. Kevin's former bedroom became *Davis' room*. A portable crib was set up between the two single beds, and the dresser was emptied of the handful of possessions that Kevin had left behind. Davis' highchair was a permanent fixture in my mother's kitchen and she reserved a drawer by the stove for Disney-themed place mats, cutlery and dishes. As Davis got a little older, he would run upstairs to search his dresser for newly purchased treasures like Toronto Maple Leafs pyjamas, a Batman t-shirt or Thomas the Train socks. Sometimes my mother would hide a new book or game or toy in the front hall closet.

When Davis was four, my mother transformed a large cardboard box into their clubhouse. She cut a door on one side of the box and a window on another. She painted a flowerbox and red bricks on the exterior and wallpapered the inside with self-adhesive shelf liner. I often arrived at her house and found Davis and my seventy-six-year-old mother squeezed into their private hideaway, enjoying a cramped snack or giggling at something that had caught their fancy.

When Davis was five and began playing hockey, my mother purchased a Fisher-Price soccer net for her basement. She spent hours on her knees or bent from her waist with a twelve inch mini hockey stick, moving up and down an imaginary skating rink, passing a ball back and forth to Davis.

Davis was six when the Japanese animated character, Pokémon, became popular. Like a million other boys his age, he became obsessed with collecting the Pokémon trading cards. I finally had to call a halt to his acquisitions. A few days after the moratorium, I arrived at my mother's house to pick up Davis but both the house and the garage were empty. It wasn't long before my mother's car pulled into the driveway with a beaming Davis in the backseat. My mother was wearing a smile as wide as her grandson's.

"Look what Grandma bought me!" he said, jumping out of the car and brandishing a handful of shiny foil packages.

The thrust of my mother's jaw told me that she had noticed my disapproval.

"It's okay, Liz, I wanted to," she said.

Davis went through a phase when he asked to sleep at his grandmother's house as often as three times a week. My mother rarely refused his request. If the sleepover was on a weeknight, I happily delivered him after dinner and returned early the next morning to drive him to school.

We took my mother with us to Davis' hockey games, music lessons, school concerts, and even some parent-teacher interviews. My mother played such a significant role in Davis' life that Jeff and I often joked that we shared joint custody with her.

As much as my mother treasured the time she spent with Davis, Davis also treasured his time with her. When he was in Grade Three, the children in his class were asked to report on one of their special memories. He wrote about the first time he and my mother went to the fall supper at my mother's church. He described how they sat at a table and waited for their number to be called so they could go up and get their meal. He said that the mashed potatoes, cooked carrots, turkey and salad were so good that he needed two helpings, and for dessert he had apple pie AND pumpkin pie.

The fall supper became an annual event for my mother and Davis that both eagerly anticipated. One year, he and my mother reluctantly agreed that Jeff and I could join them. When I glanced around the church hall I was surprised to see that there were few children in attendance. Davis was oblivious, happy to sit among the grey perms, tweed suits and buttoned-up silk blouses of my mother's friends. They were both good-natured enough about Jeff and me tagging along but we were never invited again. It was clear that their preference was to attend the supper as a duo rather than a quartet.

I phoned Art Chipman the next morning and introduced myself as Ellen Murray's daughter.

"Oh, thank goodness," he responded immediately.

I laughed.

"I gather she's been giving you a hard time?"

"You can say that again," Art said. "I tried to explain the problem we have here but she just couldn't understand. She became very angry when I told her she had written and asked for a capital payout. I asked her if there was a family member who could help her out. So she told me she had a daughter, but she refused to give me your name."

"She likes to be independent," I said. "But she asked me to talk to you now. Why don't you tell me what's been going on."

Art filled me in on the problem and what needed to be done to solve it. He also offered to contact Revenue Canada and make sure that my mother received a refund for the income tax she had paid on the capital installment that had been returned to her RRIF account. I gave him permission to do what was necessary. He sounded relieved and gladly accepted my instructions even though we both knew that I didn't have the proper authority.

"Can I leave it to you to talk to your mom?" he asked hopefully.


JUNE 2004 BREEZED into July and we fell into the idyllic pace of summer. Jeff would join Davis and me at Victoria Beach on weekends and I would return to the city occasionally to check on the house and my mother. By August, those visits to Winnipeg were less frequent. It was several days before I found out that my mother's family doctor had tried to contact me earlier in the week.

"Oh yes," Dr. Kalansky said after I had identified myself. "Your mom came to see me about her driver's license renewal." I could hear papers shuffling as she spoke. "I was calling because I wanted to know if you think she's been forgetful or confused lately."

Her voice was calm. She sounded curious rather than concerned.

I let out a deep breath. It had been three months since the altercation with Debbie Good.

"There have been a couple of things," I said.

I told Dr. Kalansky about the trees by the neighbour's driveway and the problem with my mother's RRIF. Dr. Kalansky made an occasional noise to indicate she was still listening, but mostly she just let me talk.

"So her memory is deteriorating, that's for sure," I admitted.

"Yes, that fits with what I saw," Dr. Kalansky said when I was finished. She paused and I heard papers shuffle again. "Do you know if she's taking her heart medication?"

"As far as I know."

My mother had angina but it had been controlled with medication for at least a dozen years. My own heart started beating faster.

"I haven't been monitoring it. Is there a problem with her heart?" I asked.

"Nothing new," Dr. Kalansky said. "But when I saw your mother at the beginning of the week, she told me she wasn't taking her pills. She said Dr. Rabson told her she didn't need them anymore, that she had never really had angina."

"She's been saying that for a long time – at least the part about not having angina. She doesn't like to admit she has any weaknesses." I laughed nervously. "I'm sure she must be taking her pills anyway."

My mother always kept her medication in a red seven-day pill box on her kitchen counter. I tried to remember the last time I had noticed it.

"I'm not so sure," said Dr. Kalansky. "When I pressed her, she backed down and said of course she was taking her medication. I got the sense she was just saying what she thought I wanted to hear."

"Well, that would be something my mother would do."

"I called Dr. Rabson's office – just to confirm that he hadn't taken her off the medication for some reason. He said he hadn't. He also said she cancelled her last appointment with him. That would have been in March and she hasn't rescheduled."

There was another paper shuffle and the slightest edge of concern in Dr. Kalansky's voice.

"Then I talked to her pharmacist. He said your mother ordered some pills last December and never picked them up."

Last Christmas my mother claimed that her car had been broken into and a prescription and a parcel had been stolen.

"Of course I locked the door," she had said in answer to my inquiry. "People break into locked cars all the time, you know."

A couple of weeks later my mother had asked me to help her select Christmas presents for Jeff and Davis. After a successful shopping spree at the mall we moved on to a nearby arena where Davis was playing hockey.

"I'm going to be smart this time," my mother said as she locked her purse and several shopping bags in the trunk of her car.

We had just finished dinner that evening when the telephone rang.

"Liz," my mother said in an unsteady voice. "I can't find the presents we bought today. I think someone broke into my car and stole them while we were watching Davis' hockey match."

"Do you have your purse?" I had asked.

"Just a minute."

My mother set the telephone down with a loud thud.

"Yes, it's on the dining room chair."

"Well, then I don't think the presents were stolen. No one would take the presents and leave your purse. They must be in the house somewhere."

"I've looked everywhere, Liz. They're not here."

My mother had started to cry.

The missing presents hadn't been stolen. They turned up on the ping pong table in the basement where she had always done all of her Christmas wrapping. Now, Dr. Kalansky was verifying that my mother had never been in possession of the pills she had also claimed were stolen.

"Tell me again why my mother made an appointment to see you," I asked the doctor, starting to feel queasy.

"She had a form from the Department of Motor Vehicles she needed me to fill out. Because she has angina, she has to file a medical report every two years," Dr. Kalansky told me.

I knew my mother felt that her right to drive a car was entrenched in the Charter of Rights and Freedoms. She had learned how to drive when she was just fifteen years old. Grandma, who didn't have a license herself, instructed her daughter to drive to the Miller farm road and back. My mother manoeuvred Grandpa's big Ford sedan to the Miller farm road before she realized that she didn't know how to put the car into reverse to complete the turn. When she eventually figured out how to change gears, she triumphantly returned to her waiting mother. She would sometimes brag that the next day she and Grandma drove fifteen hundred miles to visit Grandma's friend in Carman, Manitoba.

My mother soon embraced the thrill of driving whenever and wherever she wanted. She talked a lot about her driving adventures, like the times she would chauffeur a group of friends to Peterborough to watch the Peterborough Petes play hockey, or take a carload of women to Buffalo, New York, to shop.

I closed my eyes, remembering when I was nine or ten and my family drove to Vancouver in our 1965 Dodge. The first day of our holiday took us through Saskatchewan where the highway stretched forever like a giant ribbon unrolling through parched prairie and fields of wheat. My mother was driving and my father was sleeping in the passenger seat. Just before she accelerated, she caught my eye in the rear view mirror and winked. For a few minutes we were flying with the wind whistling through the open windows. When she slowed down, she straightened her hair with one hand and looked at me again in the rear view mirror. She was smiling and her eyes were shining.

"Don't tell your father," she said.

"My mother would be devastated if she lost her driver's license," I told Dr. Kalansky.

"Well, that's something Motor Vehicles decides, not you or me," she said. "I just provide them with the information they request. They take it from there. I'm going to call your mother on Monday and ask her to come back to see me. I want to talk to her about what Dr. Rabson and the pharmacist told me."

"Maybe it would be best if you didn't tell her you spoke to me," I said. "She wouldn't be happy with either of us."

I spent the rest of the day brooding about my conversation with Dr. Kalansky.

Jeff sat beside me on the futon in our screened-in porch and put his hand on my knee.

"Do you want to talk about it?"

"I do and I don't." I took a deep breath and exhaled loudly. "I just don't know how worried I should be," I said finally.

"Well," he said, "What's bothering you the most? Is it her memory?"

"Not really her memory. Forgetting she hired the tree service was pretty bad. And that RRIF cheque she forgot. But really, most of the things she forgets are no big deal. Except for Grandparents Day. And that was two years ago."

Jeff winced. "Grandparents' Day was pretty major."

Every April, Davis' school invited grandparents to attend morning classes with their grandchildren and stay for a picnic lunch. My mother had attended Grandparents' Day when Davis was in Grade One and Grade Two. Her reports on both occasions were glowing.

In 2002, when Davis was in Grade Three, my mother started talking about Grandparents' Day in February.

"I love watching Davis in his school room," she said. "He's always the first one to put his hand up to answer the teacher's questions."

The week before the big day, my mother asked me to help her select a new outfit. "I want Davis to be as proud of me as I am of him," she said.

On the eve of the event, she called to tell me that her clothes were laid out on the bed in her spare room; everything was ready so that she wouldn't be late.

"Tell Davis I'll see him in the morning."

I dialled my mother's telephone number early the next afternoon, anticipating that she would have just arrived home from Davis' school.

"So how was your morning?" I asked as soon as she picked up the receiver.

"Nothing special," my mother replied.

"Oh," I said, surprised by her cavalier dismissal of the much-awaited day. "Well, I'm sure Davis was happy to see you, anyway."

"Why would I see Davis at Reh-Fit?" she asked, referring to the exercise facility she attended three mornings a week.

"Reh-Fit!" I could hear the panic in my voice. "Didn't you go to Grandparents' Day?"

There was a moment of silence.

"No. I guess I forgot," my mother said slowly. "I knew there was something –" her voice petered out until all I could hear was heavy breathing.

I knew that she wouldn't forget Grandparents' Day on purpose but all I could think about was Davis in his hunter green blazer and grey shorts with tears rolling down his cheeks. He would have waited for my mother to arrive with all of the other grandparents, then sat alone all morning and during that special lunch wondering where she was.

"How could you do that?" I barked. I hung up the telephone halfway through my mother's explanation that *anyone could have made the same mistake.* Half a minute later I called back.

"I'm sorry, Mom," I said. "I know you –"

"You're not sorry," she interrupted. "You're always looking for an excuse to tell me how terrible I am."

It was her turn to hang up on me.

I called Davis' school and advised the secretary that I would be picking my son up early that afternoon. Forty minutes later Davis was in the back seat of my car.

"Grandma didn't mean to forget," I assured him. "She feels terrible that she let you down."

His eyes filled with tears.

"If you don't want to go to her house for a sleepover tonight Dad and I will stay home," I continued. Part of me wanted to hurt my mother by denying her Davis' company that evening. I knew that wasn't fair but I couldn't help myself.

Davis nodded thoughtfully. "No, I'll go. It'll make Grandma feel better," he said.

A few days later I tried to talk to my mother about what had happened. "Everybody forgets things sometimes. You will too when you get to be my age," she had insisted.

Jeff waited for me to continue my scrutiny of her behaviour.

"It's more than just the memory stuff," I said. "It's how she reacts to things, how she rationalizes things she can't remember. Like thinking Debbie Good cut the branches on her trees as part of a plan to take over a strip of grass. That's just crazy."

"It is crazy," Jeff said. "But it's not like she would ever admit she's having a problem."

"Right." I paused. "It's hard because physically she's so good. She does all of her own housework, she exercises, she cuts her lawn, and she'd still be shovelling snow if we didn't hire someone. How many eighty-three-year-old women do all that?"

"How many *want* to do all that?" Jeff laughed. "*I* don't even want to do all that."

I shook my head. "Sometimes she seems so normal. And other times –"

I wasn't sure how to describe those other times.

"So what do you think we should do?" Jeff asked.

"What can we do at this point?" I said. "Just wait and see."

My Special Memory    DO NOT DESTROY

My memory begins at about 7:00 pm. It is about my first time at a Fall Supper in church. First, me and my Grandma sat down and waited to be called up to get. Finally, Grandma asked me if I was having fun and I said yes. Each table got a number and if they picked your number you got to pick up a plate and get some food. The food was: mashed potatoes, cooked carrots, turkey, sausages and salad. I had everything that was served. It was so good that I had another helping. Fruit Punch was what I had to drink. After I was done my Grandma gave me a quarter to get some candy. I got about 29 candies with only 1 quarter! After that I sat in my chair and read BFG. Then came dessert! For dessert I had a piece of pumpkin pie and a pieces of yummy apple pie. Apple pie is my favourite pie in the world but I like pumpkin pie too. When I finished those pieces of pie I was so thirsty I could drink all of the Pacific Ocean. Turns out I only had a few glasses of Fruit Punch. By the time The Fall Supper was almost over I was done BFG. The other things for dessert were: chocolate cake, chocolate covered doughnuts, and a tiny bit of vanilla ice cream. I was so hoping there would be strawberry ice cream! This memory is special because it only happens once a year. I had lots of fun at the Fall Supper and if you go to a Fall Supper I hope you have lots and lots of fun too.

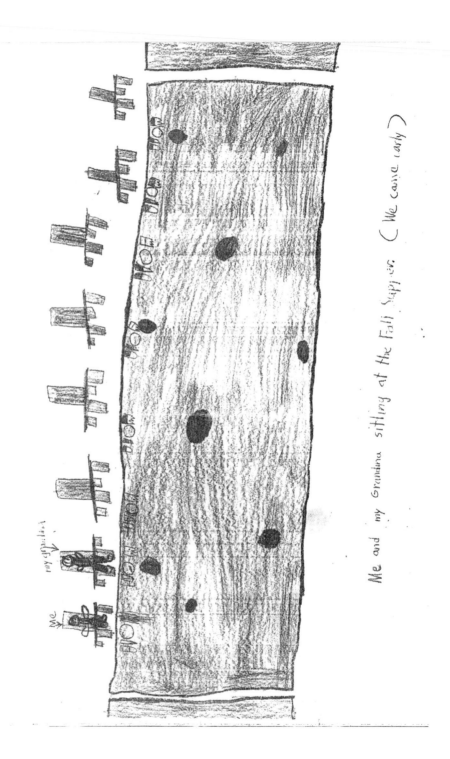

Me and my Grandma sitting at the Fall Supper. (We came early)

# Chapter Eight

**BEFORE I MET** Jeff I loved my mother more than anyone else in my world but it hadn't always been easy. She was a complicated woman, an exasperating woman who didn't like to admit when she was sad or lonely or afraid. She tried to hide her insecurity behind a tough demeanour, pretending that she was self-sufficient and didn't need anyone else to make her happy. When she told me that she loved me, she looked embarrassed, as if she had just acknowledged a weakness. She found it even more difficult to accept when she was told that she was loved.

My father's brother, Angus, was diagnosed with brain cancer in 1988 and died in the fall of 1989. On one occasion near the end of his life, my father was quiet as we drove home after a hospital visit.

"That could have been me if I hadn't married your mother," he finally said.

Angus had lived a lonely life since his wife's death twenty years earlier. My father might have suffered a similar fate if he hadn't met my mother and started a second family. I was so touched by my father's words that I repeated them to my mother a short time later.

"That makes me feel used," she said.

"It should make you feel loved!" I told her sharply. I could tell from the set of her jaw that she didn't agree.

My mother refused to acknowledge her feelings when she felt threatened, preferring to cast disdain on an interloper or avoid the topics that upset her. When Jeff and I announced our engagement after almost four years of dating, I was employed as a first-year lawyer, Jeff had just been offered a position following his articles, and we were both going to turn twenty-six in June. I assumed that my mother would be overjoyed by our news. We called my parents at their rented condominium in Florida.

My mother was quiet for what felt like a long time. Seconds pass slowly when you're listening to silence on a telephone. "Have you been to see Robin?"

she asked, referring to the minister at Holy Trinity Anglican Church. I gently
told my mother that a rabbi would be sanctifying our vows.

Jeff's parents, Max and Tonia, were Polish Jews who had survived the
Holocaust. Max and his brother escaped from a work camp and were hidden
in a barn for twenty-six months by a Polish farmwoman. Tonia was hidden
in an attic for twenty-two months by a Ukrainian soldier who was in love
with her brother's wife. The couple met in a displaced persons camp after
the war, where they lived with only the most basic amenities for two years.
Their eldest daughter was born in the camp; a baby son died as a result of
inadequate medical supplies. When they were finally allowed to immigrate
to Canada, they had little money and spoke only rudimentary English. Max
took whatever job he could find until he had saved enough money to start
a small business. He and Tonia worked in their corner grocery store twelve
hours a day, six days a week to support their five children.

Before Jeff's father died, he asked his son to promise that he wouldn't
marry me unless I converted to Judaism. I understood how important it was
for Jeff to honour his father's request.

"Won't you just meet with Robin?" my mother persisted.

When I refused again, she handed the receiver to my father.

"John, Liz and Jeff are getting married," she said flatly.

Their weekly phone call came the next Sunday morning. My mother
started the conversation with news about a seafood restaurant they had gone
to the night before, describing in detail what each of them had eaten. She
told me about a pair of slacks that she was thinking about buying in the mall.
She asked me how work was going, what the weather was like and how much
snow was in the back yard. She never mentioned my engagement. When she
finally stopped talking, I told her that I would wait until she was home to plan
my wedding. "Don't bother," she said.

For five more Sundays I tried to initiate dialogue about our plans.

"Do what you want," she said. "I'm not interested."

Finally, I gave up. I told myself that she would be different when she was home and we could discuss everything face to face.

The next several months were tense and uncomfortable. From time to time my father would ask how our wedding plans were progressing but my mother continued to maintain the position that no news was good news.

Fewer than ten weeks before the ceremony, I still hadn't started looking for a dress. Unlike some women I knew, I hadn't been dreaming about white gowns since I was a little girl but I did think that shopping for an occasion as momentous as my wedding would be something my mother and I would do together – a bonding experience to celebrate the beginning of a new stage in my life.

Visiting bridal salons alone didn't appeal to me and asking a friend to join me would have invited unwanted questions about my mother's lack of participation. I put off the search for so long that my options were limited.

In the end, I had my wedding dress made by a seamstress who had been recommended by a friend of a friend. I explained that I wanted a mermaid style with a sweetheart neckline. I said I didn't want lace or beading, and shiny fabric of any kind was absolutely forbidden. She smiled and nodded and told me that she could make me exactly what I described.

The wedding was scheduled for November 1, 1987. As the summer turned to fall, my mother presented some of the classic symptoms of depression. She developed insomnia, and began sleeping in the spare bedroom so she wouldn't disturb my father. She lost weight and she didn't have her usual amount of energy. One morning as I was getting ready for work, I went into her room to retrieve something from the closet. My mother lay awake, watching me as I searched.

"Your father is going to miss you when you move out," she said.

I knew that she meant she was going to miss me but that it was easier for her to attribute her feelings to my father. Suddenly it hit me. My mother's behaviour was about more than religion; it was also about her fear of losing me. I sat down beside her on the bed. I told her that even if I didn't marry Jeff, I wasn't going to live at home forever. I reminded her that Jeff was a good man and that he treated me well and made me happy. I speculated that if I cancelled the ceremony, I might never find anyone I loved as much as I loved Jeff. My mother's lips began to tremble. After a moment, she reached out her arms for a hug.

Shortly after that conversation my mother asked if she could come with me to the final fitting of my wedding dress.

"It's beautiful," she told me as the seamstress carefully adjusted the ruched bodice and leg-of-mutton sleeves.

Two weeks after the wedding, my mother had my white gown professionally cleaned, wrapped in acid-free tissue paper, and folded carefully into a vacuum sealed box. She printed *Liz's Wedding Dress* in large capital letters on the lid of the box and carefully stored it in the closet in my bedroom. I knew that being the keeper of my wedding dress made my mother feel closer to me; the dress was tangible evidence that I still loved and needed her even after I had married Jeff.

"It's fine right where it is," she insisted whenever I offered to take it home with me.

After we were married, Jeff's mother did her best to develop a connection between our two families but my mother preferred to maintain a distance, subtly encouraging me to do the same. Only once, at the insistence of my father, did she agree to have dinner at my mother-in-law's home.

Tonia was an eager hostess. Both Jeff and I did our best to initiate conversation. My father went out of his way to be charming. My mother adopted an artificially bright expression and directed conspiratorial glances and sly smiles across the table towards me, slyly cajoling me to participate in her shenanigans.

Jeff's mother wasn't active so my mother emphasized how many miles she walked *at least* three times a week as *only part* of her exercise regime. Jeff's mother didn't drive so my mother boasted that it would be *nothing* for her to make their annual drive from Winnipeg to Florida *all in one go.* When Jeff's mother, who was not skilled at do-it-yourself projects, marvelled at my mother's ability to reupholster simple pieces of furniture, my mother scoffed that *anyone could do it if they put their mind to it.*

Jeff and I became increasingly tense as the evening progressed. He had been aware of my mother's reluctance to socialize with his family but a small part of him had wanted to believe that I was exaggerating the extent of her antipathy. Once he had the opportunity to watch and listen to her in action, he understood that I had been telling him the truth: our mothers were not going to have a close relationship. My mother would simply not allow it. Over the next several years, I sought to avoid contact with my mother-in-law, knowing that if we became close, my mother would make it difficult for me in whatever way she could.

DEMENTIA IS CUNNING. Its symptoms creep up on unwilling victims, hiding behind more normal behaviour. In retrospect, I should have recognized my mother's impaired thinking, loss of memory and bouts of depression much sooner, collecting the signs like items on the list in a scavenger hunt. Of course, in a scavenger hunt the participants are eager to find what they are seeking. My father's death, my fight with cancer and the tension over Falcon Lake had left me emotionally drained and I didn't want any added burdens. It was easier to dismiss my concerns and simply accept my mother's unpredictable or manipulative behaviour.

Three years ago in the spring of 2001, I was driving my mother home on one of the main arteries in the south end of Winnipeg.

"That's where my car went into the ditch the other day," she had told me, pointing to the side of the four-lane highway. "All of a sudden the steering wheel turned. It was like the car had a mind of its own."

"Are you sure you didn't get distracted or fall asleep for a second?" I asked, startled by her cavalier admission.

"The steering wheel just turned," she insisted.

I had suggested that it was time for Jeff to take the car in for an inspection.

Her car was pronounced mechanically sound after only a few small adjustments but a couple of weeks later, my mother told me that she was driving down the same four-lane highway when once again the steering wheel turned *all on its own*. The car went over the curb, crossed the wide boulevard that separated the opposing traffic, and finally came to a stop facing north in the middle of the southbound lanes.

Soon after, she approached Jeff with a coquettish smile and asked him if he had time to go car shopping. I had been trying to persuade my mother for almost a year to replace her 1989 Pontiac but she had always refused. I allowed myself to believe that she had concocted the problems with her car to justify her change of heart.

Other unsettling incidents involved memory lapses that seemed more than mere forgetfulness. My mother's baking tins were always full of homemade treats and her raisin cookies were a family favourite. Instead of adding whole raisins to the butterscotch-flavoured dough, my mother used an old-fashioned meat grinder to mince the fruit. My job as assistant baker had been to turn the handle on the grinder as my mother pushed the raisins into the rotating blade. When I decided to add the cookies to my list of Christmas baking in 2002, my mother's forehead wrinkled slightly as she considered my request.

"I don't know what recipe you're talking about," she said.

I described how she clamped the meat grinder to the breadboard so it wouldn't move while we were working, and how she refused to let me feed the raisins into the mouth of the machine because she was afraid I would hurt my fingers. She shook her head and shrugged.

I told her how we had sung *Patty cake, patty cake, baker's man*, as we patted the dough into a log, and I had placed the discs onto the cookie sheet after she had cut them.

"I don't know what you're talking about, Elizabeth," she repeated, her tone almost angry.

I was astounded. As a child I had loved those cookies as much for the making as for the eating. How could she possibly forget their existence? The incident had left me with a feeling of disquiet.

My mother had always applauded our decision to send Davis to a private school. To reinforce her support she presented me with a cheque for one thousand dollars every year as a contribution towards her grandson's tuition.

"Just wait a minute, Liz," she said one day in June 2003, as I was preparing to leave her house. She went into the dining room and slid open the glass door of the china cabinet. When she returned to the kitchen she was holding an envelope with my name printed on it in capital letters.

"This is for Davis' school," she told me.

"Thanks Mom, but you know it's not necessary," I said.

"I know, but I want to," she replied.

When my mother called me the next morning, her voice was cold.

"I want you to return what you took from my house yesterday," she said.

"What are you talking about, Mom?"

"Don't play dumb with me, Elizabeth. You know what you took – that cheque from the buffet in the dining room."

"You mean the cheque that you gave me? The one that was in the envelope with my name on the front?"

"I don't remember giving you the cheque," my mother replied slowly. Her tone had warmed a little but I was too irritated to be conciliatory. I told her that I had to drive Davis to school and abruptly ended our conversation.

Half an hour later, I could hear the faint chime of the telephone as I approached the door that led from the attached garage into the back hallway of our house. The sound stopped and then started again after only a few seconds. My guess was that my mother had been dialling my telephone number the whole time that I had been away.

"Liz," my mother said through her tears. "I'm sorry. I know you wouldn't have just taken the cheque. I don't know what comes over me sometimes."

Over the years there had been other signs that would have revealed a deeper concern if I had been inclined to examine them collectively. Once, after I suggested that she shouldn't cut the lawn with her electric mower if the grass was wet, she told me that it didn't matter whether she lived or died. When I proposed that she should talk to a doctor if that's really how she felt, she retorted that I *should just forget about it since I didn't care about her anyway*. Instead of pursuing the matter, I allowed myself to be seduced by the fact that most of the time when I visited my mother or watched her with Davis or took her shopping she was the same as she always had been – sometimes contrary but invariably strong and determined.

My mother continued to balk at any reference to our cottage and I stopped issuing invitations since they only seemed to fuel her resentment. In August 2003, my late Uncle Peter's daughter, Carol Winstanley, provided a face-saving opportunity for my mother to change her mind.

"Would you like to bring her here for the day on Saturday?" I suggested tentatively as soon as my mother told me that my cousin was coming from Hamilton for the weekend and wanted to see us.

"No way! If she wants to go somewhere we can go to my cottage."

I offered to drive to the city but said that Davis and Jeff would want to stay at the beach. My mother insisted that Carol needed to see Davis and Jeff as well as me. I again pointed out the easy solution. My mother repeated her vow that she would never come to Victoria Beach. I started to cry. She hung up on me.

My mother called back a few minutes later with a new idea. She said that she would take Carol to Falcon Lake on Saturday for the day and bring her to Victoria Beach on Sunday. She assured me that they would arrive bright and early in the morning. It sounded like a lot of unnecessary travel when Carol was only in Winnipeg for the weekend but I appreciated my mother's compromise and agreed to the plan.

By one o'clock Sunday afternoon, we had neither seen nor heard from my mother and Carol. I started to worry. At two o'clock my mother called and said they had just returned from Falcon Lake and were preparing to embark on the ninety minute drive to Victoria Beach. They arrived at our cottage at five-thirty, with just enough time for dinner and a short visit.

"I want to be back on the road well before eight o'clock," my mother advised as I leaned closer to give her a hug hello.

My cousin and I washed lettuce and chopped vegetables for a salad while my mother sat on the front deck with Davis and Jeff. In a low voice, Carol gave me a report on the time she had spent with my mother. She said that they were getting into the car to leave for Falcon Lake Saturday morning when my mother suddenly insisted that she had to mow the lawn and wash the kitchen floor. A late start turned the day trip to Falcon Lake into an overnight stay with more time wasted Sunday morning. When they finally returned to Winnipeg, my mother wanted to mow the lawn again before leaving for our cottage. My cousin's eyes grew wide with fear as she recounted the trip to Victoria Beach.

"Driving here was a nightmare!" Carol confided. "At least twice I was sure we were going to die."

My mother had passed cars on the single lane highway right in front of oncoming traffic. Her highway driving had always been aggressive but this behaviour was out of character, even for her. I was nervous about my mother driving back to the city and I made her promise to phone me the moment she arrived home.

"Don't be silly," my mother responded. "I've been driving on highways for over fifty years."


CANCER HAD CHANGED my life in ways I couldn't have contemplated. After my recurrence, the surgery, radiation, chemotherapy and a year-long biologic treatment collected their physical and emotional toll but I took comfort in the process of conquering the invasive cells. When my treatment was finally complete in the spring of 1999, the battle was over and the waiting began.

The missing sternocleidomastoid muscle in the left side of my neck meant that my neck, jaw and upper back were chronically tight. Headaches and difficulty speaking became routine occurrences. Regular massages and physiotherapy provided only temporary relief. I gradually became accustomed to the pressure of an invisible assailant's hands around my neck but that didn't make it any more comfortable.

The chance of a further recurrence was higher in the first five years and Jeff and I struggled not to worry that every cough or sore throat I experienced was the precursor of another cancer diagnosis. When I regained the strength I had lost during the eighteen months of my treatment, I had to decide if I should return to work. I knew that the strain in my neck and upper back would be exacerbated by sitting at a desk and I would have to spend the hours after work resting rather than participating in family activities. More importantly, the looming concern of a further recurrence made me want to spend as much time as possible with Davis. Giving up the practice of law wasn't an easy decision but it was the only decision that made sense.

When Davis was home, I was happy. When he was in school, I was lonely and missed the social contact and intellectual challenge of the office. My health was a priority, so I filled my mornings with exercise; afternoons were more problematic.

I enjoyed meeting my employed friends for lunch but I felt superfluous when they were obliged to rush back to their desks. I desperately missed the stimulation and chaotic bustle of my pre-cancer life.

Before cancer I was fluid, able to juggle the competing and ever-changing demands inherent in a busy career as well as an active family life. I didn't conform to a rigid schedule; an impromptu plan or spontaneous invitation meant an opportunity to fit more into an already full calendar. After cancer, I needed to control my world. A last-minute adjustment to my timetable, however inconsequential, made me anxious and often reduced me to tears. Structure was my guilty pleasure; packaging my day into neat little squares of what was going to happen next was essential for my emotional well-being.

Dementia was not something that I could control. I pushed away the questions that Dr. Kalansaky's call had raised, preferring not to confront the fear that my mother was in at least the early stages of a disease. I simply couldn't handle another family crisis.

I never liked Kalansky the doctor Liz got me to go to about four years ago. Last August when I went she checked my eyes and gave me a body check then said to go to another office for a blood test. When I first went into her office she started some sort of conversation not connected with me, nor interesting ~~so when she was finished~~

This went on for quite a while, and all of a sudden she asked what number did I say at the beginning of this long drawn out conversation, so I said I didn't remember - I had to go to another office for a blood test - went back to her office - waiting room ~~was full~~ had a number of people in it - I waited ~~ing~~ around for awhile then thought well she didn't say she required to see me after the blood test so came home - next morning she called me - sounded very angry and told me I should have gone back after the blood test, and wanted to see me at her office at 3:30 that day -when I got down there I asked her was there something wrong with the blood test and she said no - silence for a while - then she said, same as her angry morning conversation, about me not coming back to her office- so I asked her if I had to have another blood test and she nonchalantly said no

# Manitoba

| Transportation and Government Services Driver and Vehicle Licencing 1075 Portage Avenue Winnipeg, MB  R3G 0S1 CANADA | Medical Records Bureau des dossiers médicaux Tel. / Tél. (204) 945-7386 | Transports et Services gouvernementaux Permis et immatriculations 1075, avenue Portage Winnipeg (Manitoba)  R3G 0S1 CANADA |

CERTIFIED

Ellen M. Murray                                           November 4, 2004
42 Thatcher Dr                                            LIC: MURRAEM797KG
Winnipeg MB  R3T 2L3

### Notice of Suspension - Section 28(3) of The Highway Traffic Act

We have received information which indicates your medical condition may be such as to impair your ability to operate a motor vehicle.  In view of this, we regret to advise that your driver's licence and right to obtain a licence, are hereby suspended pursuant to Section 28(3) *The Highway Traffic Act* commencing on November 12, 2004.  Please understand that this decision was made in the best interest of your safety and the safety of the general public.

You are requested to return your driver's licence certificate on or immediately after the date of suspension to the above address, unless you have already surrendered it.  You may retain the photo identification card.  Any operation of a motor vehicle after this suspension comes into force will be an infraction of *The Highway Traffic Act* and the vehicle you are operating will be impounded.  In addition, any operation of an implement of husbandry, special mobile machine or tractor on a provincial highway, or highway within a city, town or village will be an infraction of *The Highway Traffic Act*.

**This suspension will remain in force indefinitely or until you have complied with the following requirement(s):**

Pass the written test and a vision screening at your nearest Driver Testing location.  A driver's handbook will arrive under separate cover for your review.  See attached letter for specific instruction.

Furnish Medical Records with a driving assessment to be completed by an occupational therapist from the Rehabilitation Hospital, Health Sciences Centre, Winnipeg.  (You will be notified when an appointment can be made once the physician's referral is received by Medical Records).  This assessment will not be completed until the above requirement(s) have been approved by the Division.

**Once the medical requirement(s) have been complied with and you have been notified the medical standards have been met, no licence will be issued until you:**

Satisfactorily complete driver examinations.

If you have any questions concerning the above action(s) being taken by this Division contact Medical Records at the above address or telephone (204) 985-1900.  Outside Winnipeg, call toll free 1-866-617-6676.

Thank you for your cooperation in this important matter.

Enclosure

M.J. Zyluk
Registrar of Motor Vehicles

/tn                          **Please see reverse. / Veuillez voir au verso.**
Une traduction de ce document peut être obtenue en français sur demande.

# Manitoba

| Transportation and<br>Government Services | Driver and Vehicle Licencing<br>Medical Records Section | 1075 Portage Ave<br>Winnipeg MB  R3G 0S1 |
|---|---|---|

Dear Physician:

Your patient is required to have a driving assessment at the Driving Assessment & Management Program, Rehabilitation Hospital, Health Sciences Centre, Winnipeg.  Please complete this referral form and mail to Medical Records at the above address or fax (204) 953-4992.

**THIS REFERRAL IS VALID FOR ONE YEAR.**

Patient's name:   Ellen M. Murray                      Maiden name:

Address:   42 THATCHER DR.                      Postal code:   R3T 2L3

Phone: (home):   269-7937                      (business):

Date of birth:   07 MAY 21                      Driver's licence #:   MURRAEM797KG

MB health #:   193420                      Sex:   F.

P.H.I.N. #:   102 261 265                      Next of kin:

Occupation/School:   retired

Primary language:   English

PRIMARY DIAGNOSIS:   possible early dementia   MMSE 27/30

Date of onset:   Aug/05

Other relevant problems and/or contraindications to driving:

Medication:   ASA, Nadolol 80 god, Nitro patch.

Further comments:

PATIENTS RELEASE:
I hereby authorize my physician to release this medical information to the Registrar.

Date:   Dec 1/04                      Patient's signature:  X Ellen M. Murray

Referring physician (print):   G. KALANSKY   B.K.

Physician's address:   250-2025 CORYDON                      Physician's signature

Phone:   989-6040                      Date of referral:   Dec 1/04

**NOTE TO DRIVER:**
After all medical requirements have been completed and approved, this referral will be forwarded to the Occupational Therapy Department and they will contact you for an appointment.

**NOTE TO DRIVER AND PHYSICIAN:**
THE RECEIPT OF THIS COMPLETED REFERRAL AUTHORIZES THE EXCHANGE OF ALL THE DRIVER'S MEDICAL AND LICENCING INFORMATION ON FILE BETWEEN THE DIVISION OF DRIVER AND VEHICLE LICENCING AND THE OCCUPATIONAL THERAPIST AT THE REHABILITATION HOSPITAL.

Ce document peut être obtenu français sur demande.  Composez le 945-7386.

# Manitoba

| | | |
|---|---|---|
| **Transportation and Government Services Driver and Vehicle Licencing** 1075 Portage Avenue Winnipeg, MB  R3G 0S1 CANADA | Medical Records *Dossiers médicaux* (204)-945-7386 | *Transports et Services gouvernementaux Permis et immatriculations* 1075, avenue Portage Winnipeg (MB) R3G 0S1 *CANADA* |

Ellen M. Murray
42 Thatcher Dr
Winnipeg MB  R3T 2L3

November 4, 2004
LIC: MURRAEM797KG

Dear Ms. Murray:

We have received the medical report completed on your behalf.

You may now appear for a written test and a vision screening test at your nearest Driver Testing location. Please take your corrective lenses if applicable. No driver's licence will be issued at this time.

Once you have passed the written and vision screening tests and the enclosed physician's referral is received by Medical Records, you will be advised by the Occupational Therapy Department, Rehabilitation Hospital, Health Science Centre, Winnipeg regarding an appointment for the driving assessment. We will receive a copy of the results once the assessment has been completed and you will be notified.

Further information regarding these instruction(s) may be obtained by calling (204) 985-1900. Outside Winnipeg, call toll free 1-866-617-6676.

TO APPLICANT/DRIVER:  PLEASE BRING THIS LETTER WITH YOU TO THE DRIVER TESTING OFFICE BETWEEN THE HOURS OF 8:30 A.M. - 3:00 P.M., MONDAY THROUGH FRIDAY.

TO DRIVER TESTING STAFF:  PLEASE RECORD RESULTS AND FAX TO MEDICAL RECORDS.  YOU MUST RETURN THIS ORIGINAL LETTER TO THE APPLICANT/DRIVER.  NO DRIVER'S LICENCE TO BE ISSUED.

| Date | Exam Type | Results | Ex's No. | Place |
|---|---|---|---|---|
| | | | | |
| | | | | |
| | | | | |

| | | Right | Left | Both |
|---|---|---|---|---|
| X | Vision without corrective lenses | | | |
| | Vision with corrective lenses | | | |
| X | Field of vision (in degrees) | ° | ° | ° |
| X | Colour perception | | | |

Yours truly,

Enclosure

*Macdonald*

Victoria Macdonald, R.N., BScN.
Supervisor of Medical Records

1252-06-B6  MG-13080 (R-08/02)
Ce document peut être obtenu en français sur demande.
/tn

Medical Records Assessment & Management Program
Rehabilitation Hospital
Health Sciences Centre
Winnipeg, Manitoba

Re: where it says Date of Onset August 5 - possible
early dementia
    I went to Kalansky for a check up, she sent me to
another office for a blood test, ~~I went back to her~~
~~office,~~ I went back to her office and waited which
had a number of patients waiting and I felt I'd be
at the end of the line - I did wait for awhile - then
decided to come home as I was going out for dinner at
    5:30 - I didn't like to bother the girl at the desk she
    was busy with others, went outside for awhile then
    decided to come home
there were a few people ahead of me (as usual a wait
always seems endless) - I realize I should have gone
to her clerk to mention I had plans for the evening,
starting 5:30 pm. Went outside for awhile again and
    decided to come home
    The next morning at 10:00 AM she phoned me (not
    in the best of moods) told me I was to be down at
her office by 3:30 pm. Went down, she was outside her
office so had a very short conversation, then she said
you can go now. So I left - the next thing was this
    early dementia notice from driver & Vehicle Licensing
    re medical suspension - I could not see that what I
    did was possible early dementia, stupidity perhaps
- but -

# Chapter Nine

IN EARLY NOVEMBER 2004, I was helping Davis study for a test when my mother called about a letter she had received earlier that day.

"It says I can't have a driver's license anymore. It says I'm too sick or something."

She sniffed.

"I don't know why anybody would say I was too sick to drive. Can Jeff come over and have a look at this, please? Right now?"

I had been dreading this moment for three months. I pictured my mother sitting at the kitchen table with the phone in one hand and the letter in the other.

"Sure, Mom, he'll be right there."

Jeff was reading a *New Yorker* magazine in front of the fireplace. He looked up when he heard me offer his services.

"Her driver's license has been suspended," I told him.

"Your poor mother," he said, shaking his head when he returned home.

"You know, she usually looks ten years younger than she is. Tonight she looked ten years older. I feel so bad for her."

He sat down beside me and sighed.

"So what did the letter really say?" I asked.

"There were two letters. One said that her license was suspended immediately for medical reasons. The other was about a form she had to take to her doctor. She couldn't understand it. She kept asking what she had done wrong." Jeff sighed again. "It was so sad. I tried to tell her she didn't do anything wrong, but she just didn't get it."

He stood up and put another log on the fire.

"So what happens now?" I asked.

"Well, I took her license. She was supposed to mail it in to Motor Vehicles but I wasn't sure she would do it." He pulled the license out of his pocket and tossed it onto a side table. "Oh, and she wants me to figure out who she can sue so she can get her license back."

I grimaced and asked if there was any way that she could apply to have the suspension lifted.

"Yeah, the letters outline the process. I told her you would talk to her about it tomorrow." He pressed his lips together and looked at me. "Do you really think it's a good idea, though?"

"I don't know. The problem is that what's right for my mother isn't necessarily what's right."

"I know," Jeff said. "I know."

The next day, I found my mother sitting on the couch peering out the front window, watching for me. I hadn't told her specifically when I would be coming. I wondered how long she had been waiting.

"How are you doing, Mom?"

I sat beside her and put my arm around her shoulders. She was dressed in royal blue wool pants and a matching blue and pink mohair cardigan. Instead of the slippers that she customarily wore inside the house, she had on black leather shoes. Her coat and purse were lying on the coffee table in front of her.

"I'm okay," she said. "I'm ready to go get my driver's license back. Jeff said you would take me today." She stood up and reached for her coat and purse. "What are we waiting for?"

"Hold on a minute, Mom."

I tried to keep my voice calm and reassuring.

My mother turned to look at me.

"What do you mean? I thought we were going to go tell somebody – you know, whoever we need to tell – that I'm not sick. That there's been a mistake and I should get my driver's license back." Her voice was getting higher and angrier as she spoke. "That's what Jeff said."

"Mom, look, I need to read that letter and find out what has to be done. There's going to be a process we have to follow."

I waited while my mother stared at me. Her forehead crinkled and her lower lip moved forward slightly.

"Do you have the letter handy, Mom?" I prodded gently.

My mother's lip protruded into a full-blown pout.

"I don't know." She sat back down on the couch and began rummaging through her purse. "It was here earlier. I know I read it this morning." She put her purse back on the coffee table. "But where is it now?" She covered her face with her hands and began to cry. "Why is this happening to me?"

I put my arms around her and hugged her hard.

"It's okay. We'll get through this."

Even as I spoke the words I was afraid that they weren't true. As I held my sobbing mother, I remembered the day when my Grade Two teacher had ridiculed me in front of the class for having an unusually messy desk. I was mortified. I walked home for lunch as slowly as I could, hoping to put off telling my mother about my humiliating experience. I held back my tears as my mother set out our grilled cheese sandwiches and settled herself at her place at the table. The four neat squares of sandwich on my plate slowly blurred into one and I began to weep. I told my mother my sorry tale in gasps as I continued to cry. She pushed her chair back from the table and held out her arms. I sat on her knee as she gently rocked back and forth until I was finally able to dry my tears.

"That teacher's going to hear from me," she said. "She's not going to get away with talking to my girl like that."

I still remember how secure I felt, confident that my mother's love would keep me safe forever.

The strength of my mother's love had also comforted me during the years I suffered from nightmares. From the time I was six until I turned eight or nine, I frequently woke up in the middle of the night and imagined that a burglar had broken into the house and was stealthily creeping towards my bedroom. After whimpering to myself for several minutes, I would call out for my mother. No matter what the time or how often it happened, she would come running, crawling into my single bed and holding me tight until I fell back asleep.

I wished that I could do something now to shield her from the hurt she was feeling, just as she had protected me when I was a child.

After a few minutes she pushed me away and wiped her eyes with a tissue that she had tucked into the cuff of her sweater.

"It's just not right," she said. "I didn't do anything wrong. I should be able to have my driver's license."

I took a quick look at the papers on the coffee table. The letter wasn't there so I got up and searched the pile of papers in the kitchen.

"Here's the letter, Mom," I called. "Let's see what has to be done."

The reinstatement process required my mother to have a medical form completed by her family physician, to pass a written driver's test, and, if that was successful, to pass an in-car test with an occupational therapist. I knew the medical form would be a problem. Dr. Kalansky had already provided a report that questioned whether my mother should have a driver's license but to dissuade my mother from starting the process would be a no-win proposition for me.

"You'll have to see Dr. Kalansky and ask her to fill out this form," I told her. "In the meantime, I'll help you study for your written test."

Two weeks later my mother called. She sounded angry rather than defeated.

"Can you come over and look at this? I know who's behind this mess about my driver's license," she said. "It's that Dr. Kalansky. She's always hated me." The previous week, I had taken my mother to the doctor to ask her to complete the form required by the department of Driver and Vehicle Licensing. My mother had been astute enough to ask for a copy.

When I arrived, she was standing in front of the ironing board. A laundry basket full of towels and bed sheets was sitting on a chair beside her. She didn't look up when I entered the room. I watched her select a towel from the basket, press her iron over one side and then the other, and fold the rectangle into a neat square. Her movements were strong and purposeful.

The practice written tests I had downloaded covered the kitchen table. A pad of lined paper and a pen sat at my mother's usual place setting, along with an official driver's license handbook. It appeared that my mother had been reviewing the handbook and the practice tests before the mail arrived with the letter from Dr. Kalansky's office.

"There's that Kalansky's report." My mother motioned to the counter with her head. "She says I have debenture."

She held a towel by two sides and snapped it taut before she folded it. She took another towel from the basket and resumed ironing.

I retrieved the report and began reading. Dr. Kalansky had written *possible early dementia* in the box titled *Prognosis*. I suspected that she would have used stronger language if my mother hadn't asked for a copy. I kept that thought to myself.

"Dementia, not debenture," I corrected her. I knew immediately I should have kept that to myself as well.

"Dementia, then." My mother was almost spitting she was so angry. "Whatever it is, it means the doctor thinks I'm simple." She turned to face me, still holding the iron. Her hand shook.

To my mother, dementia wasn't a disease, it was a judgment. Florence Smith was an elderly spinster my mother had met when she first joined the Altar Guild at Holy Trinity Anglican Church. When Florence had passed away several years earlier, my mother was incensed that the obituary attributed the death to dementia. "There was never anything wrong with Florence's mind," my mother had said. "She always knew me."

"Dementia is just the medical term for getting a little forgetful," I told her now. "It doesn't mean the doctor thinks you're simple. Anyway, it says *possible* and *early*. That means she's not even sure."

"Elizabeth," she said, "It means she thinks I'm crazy, and you know it."

My mother finished folding the towel that she had been ironing and came over to the kitchen table. She waved her arm at the practice tests and the driver's handbook.

"I guess I don't need these any more. I'm never going to get my driver's license back now."

She gathered the papers together and tossed them into the garbage can.

By my next visit, the practice tests had been retrieved and were strewn across the kitchen table along with several pieces of crumpled lined paper.

"Can you quiz me?" she asked. "I might as well keep studying and try to write that test."

I looked at the pad of paper in front of her. She was writing out the answers to the test questions in long hand after consulting the handbook.

"Mom, you don't need to do all this work. The test will be multiple choice, just like these practice ones. Just circle the right answer."

I had explained the format when I brought her the practice tests, and on at least two other occasions since.

"You mean I won't have to write out the answers? I just have to choose one from the list?" She picked up one of the tests and examined it more closely. "One of the answers is right and the rest are wrong?"

I took the test she was holding.

"Let's go through this and try to answer everything. When we run into one we don't know, we'll check the handbook."

My mother carefully read each question and answer out loud but even the obvious answers eluded her. I doodled on a piece of paper and tried to curb my desire to drum my fingers on the table. I welcomed the activity when my mother wanted to walk around the neighbourhood to see which signs she could properly identify. I decided to call a time out when she wanted to use a measuring tape to help her decide the right distance for a car to stop in front of a stop sign.

Back in the kitchen, my mother sat in her chair and crossed her arms over her chest.

"You know, I've been thinking about that Dr. Kalansky and trying to figure out why she would write that report. I haven't even seen her since the summer."

My mother had told me this story many times over the last week. I had stopped reminding her that we had gone together to see Dr. Kalansky and that we had asked her to complete the medical form my mother now found so offensive.

"It all started in August when I didn't go back to see her after my blood test. She examined me – I can't even remember why I was there in the first place – and then sent me down the hall for a blood test. I was supposed to go back and see her, but there was such a long line of people in her waiting room and I wanted to get home. So I just left. And then she phoned me the next day and told me get back here right away."

My mother shook her head in disgust.

"Her voice was so angry. I've never heard a doctor speak that way before."

I bit my lip to keep from saying anything.

"When I went back, she was really nasty. I tried to explain why I hadn't waited. She didn't want to hear anything I had to say." My mother paused and shook her head again. "She wrote that report out of spite. I know she did. Besides, she's always hated me."

"Mom, why would Dr. Kalansky hate you? She barely even knows you," I said. "Doctors don't write reports out of spite."

My mother walked into the living room and sat on the couch looking out the window. When I sat beside her, she turned away from me.

"Look, I'm not saying her concerns were right. I'm just saying I don't think Dr. Kalansky wrote the report out of spite or because she hates you."

My mother continued to ignore me. Eventually she said, "Well, you would think that, wouldn't you, Elizabeth?"


I KNEW THAT it would be difficult for my mother to adjust to life without a driver's license but the reality was so much worse than I had imagined. She would often decline my first offer to take her to the grocery store or the bank or the drug store, warding off my suggestion with *it's just up the street* or *I can walk.* Sometimes, when I pointed out the advantage of not having to lug bags of groceries home, or reminded her that her destination was several miles away, she would sigh and concede. *Since I insisted, she guessed* she would allow me to accompany her. On other occasions she would get angry and demand that I stop trying to *interfere in her life.*

Shopping had once been something that we enjoyed doing together. During the summer before I entered Grade Nine, I took the bus to Polo Park Shopping Centre two or three times a week to meet my mother for her lunch hour. The ladies in her office greeted me with questions about my achievements or interests, evidence that my mother had been bragging about me in my absence. She would eat a sandwich during her morning coffee break so we would have as much time as possible to wander in and out of the stores in the mall together.

When I was very young, I would trail after my mother as she browsed for bargains in the women's fashions at the Eaton's store on Portage Avenue and then stop for lunch at the coffee shop on the third floor. My order was always a ham sandwich with lettuce and a chocolate milkshake that came to the table in a stainless steel cylinder; my mother ordered a salmon sandwich and a pot of tea. After lunch I would sit on the floor in the book department and read Nancy Drew mysteries while my mother continued to shop. We used to laugh about the time she drove halfway home before she realized that I was still waiting for her to retrieve me.

Shopping with my mother had become a penance rather than a pleasure. As she struggled to protect her independence, she only became more intransigent.

"I may have left a grey, wool coat with you earlier in the week," I overheard her say one winter morning as I took off my boots at the front door. "No, I don't have a ticket, but I think –"

She looked up and jumped slightly when I entered the kitchen.

"I'll have to call you back."

She hung up the telephone with a decisive click. I noticed the Yellow

Pages were opened to a two page spread of dry cleaners.

"What's up?" I asked.

My mother flipped the directory closed. The corners of her mouth turned down and she glared at me.

"You don't have to know everything," she said.

She walked to the counter where her breakfast dishes were drying on a rack and began putting them in the cupboard. The dishes banged together as she worked. When she was finished, she turned towards me, arms across her chest and fists clenched.

"Wanda drove me to the dry cleaners so I could get my coat cleaned. But I can't find the ticket and I don't know which dry cleaner it was. I wanted you to take me to pick it up today."

"No problem. Just call Wanda and ask her –"

"I don't want to do that, Elizabeth," she interrupted. "It was somewhere on Pembina Highway, I know that." She sat down at the table and rubbed her hands over her eyes. "It's different when you're driving. You just know where you're going."

A week later my mother asked me to take her to the drugstore. She was carrying a plastic bag full of used containers that she had collected from her bathroom, some of which were at least several years old.

A sales assistant in the cosmetics department hurried over to us when my mother pulled a grimy bottle of foundation out of her bag. The bottle appeared to be almost full, not surprisingly, since I had never known my mother to use foundation. When I was young, lipstick and powder were her only make-up essentials. Blusher – which was called rouge – and a touch of mascara were reserved for special occasions.

"I'd like to replace this."

My mother held the bottle at arm's length. The woman took it from my mother's hand.

"We carry Max Factor products, but this particular line is no longer being made." She smiled. "I can help you find something else if you like."

She moved towards a display that featured several brands.

My mother and I trailed behind her.

The woman pulled two sample bottles from the shelf. She opened one and squeezed foundation onto a disposable make-up sponge.

"Let me just try a little here, on your jaw line." She reached out and patted my mother's face gently with the sponge. "You've got lovely blue eyes, Dear," she said as she worked.

My mother stiffened and jerked her head away from the woman's hand.

"I just want the same as I had before," my mother said.

"How about that one?" I suggested, pointing to the bottle in the woman's right hand. It didn't matter which we chose, my mother wouldn't be wearing it anyway.

The woman looked relieved when I hooked my right arm through my mother's left arm and led her away from the cosmetics department.

"Okay, Mom, what's next?"

My mother pulled a tube of Crest toothpaste out of the bag. The bottom of the tube was rolled almost to the top, and a crusty ring of paste circled the lid. Like the foundation, it looked to be several years old.

"I need some of this," my mother said. She studied the tube. "But I think I'm using something else right now." She rummaged in the bag and came up with a newer looking container of Sensodyne. "Here, I'm going to need some of this, too."

I looked at both tubes.

"Why don't we just get that?" I suggested, pointing to the still half full Sensodyne.

My mother pursed her lips. She turned and scanned the rows of toothpaste containers.

"I want both," she said.

We went through the same process with every other toiletry: shampoo and conditioner, hairspray, bubble bath, hand soap, cotton balls, tissues and nail polish. We were heading to the cashier with an overflowing basket when my mother saw the laundry detergent on sale.

"I'd better get some of this washing soap," she said, reaching for the jumbo, family-sized bottle and cradling it in her arms like a baby.

"There's enough there to last a family of four for a year. You don't need that much," I told her.

"I'm getting this." She narrowed her eyes and squared her shoulders. "Now I can't drive, I need to stock up."

In the car on the way home, my mother told me she was going to cancel her plans to go to the Winnipeg Senior Men's Choir Christmas concert. The husband of one of her friends was in the choir and group of women from my mother's church had been going to the concert for years. My mother was usually the driver.

"If I can't drive, I don't want to go," she said.

"That's silly, Mom. You should still go. Either Jeff or I will drive you, or you can take a taxi. Whatever you prefer."

"I'd prefer to drive myself."

I stole a look at her face. Her eyes were narrowed again.

"Anyway, I was supposed to pick up Audrey and Betty. What am I going to tell them if I can't?"

"You could tell them you don't want to drive in the dark. You could tell them your car is getting fixed." I paused. "Or you could just tell them the truth. They're your friends. They're not going to care."

My mother's head was turned and she was staring out her side window.

"Well, I care," she said. "I care."

# Chapter Ten

**MY BROTHER, KEVIN,** and I had never had a close relationship. When we were teenagers, he treated me as a near stranger, offering a mumbled hello or barely perceptible nod when it was absolutely necessary. If we happened to be in the basement together watching the only television in the house, he occasionally acknowledged me by clearing his throat and scowling in my direction. More often, he ignored me completely.

In retaliation, I took every opportunity to provoke a response. Sometimes, I would try to force Kevin to talk to me by asking nonsensical questions or making inane comments. When I could get close enough to actually touch him, I would repeatedly poke my finger in his shoulder until he lost his temper or left the room. I persisted even though I knew my behaviour was annoying, justifying my actions as legitimate attempts to interact with my brother.

We did manage to forge a shaky alliance for a few years. I met Jeff, whom Kevin seemed to like, and Kevin started dating Heather. Kevin was my only wedding attendant; when Kevin and Heather were married he asked me to give the toast to the groom.

Heather and I were pregnant at the same time and even though they had moved to the United States where Kevin was finishing his training as a physician, we had weekly telephone conferences to keep updated on each other's progress. The birth of Kevin and Heather's daughter, Megan, six weeks before I had Davis, marked a high point in our relationship.

When my cancer recurred in October 1997, it was Kevin who advised us to seek a second opinion at MD Anderson Cancer Center in Houston. He even offered to accompany Jeff and me to ensure that we asked the right questions and obtained the right information. When the timing of the consultation didn't work with Kevin's schedule, I suggested that he could speak to the doctors on the telephone instead.

Kevin didn't refuse to contact the other doctors; he just didn't do it.

When he came home at Christmas that year, we had an ugly confrontation. He told me that he *wasn't my personal physician* and that he couldn't *decide my treatment for me*. I felt angry and betrayed.

I finished a seven-week regime of radiation and chemotherapy in the middle of January 1998. Four weeks later, I began a twelve-month biologic treatment of interferon and cis-retinoic acid. I had been tired during chemotherapy and radiation; I was now completely exhausted. At the end of June, after four and a half months on the biologic treatment, I was struggling to get through the day. Jeff and I tried to ensure Davis' routines didn't suffer as a result of my illness but by the time Kevin and his family came home in August for a visit, I was in rough shape.

As in the previous two years, I scheduled Davis' birthday party for the week that Kevin was in Winnipeg, hoping his children, Megan and Graeme, would be able to attend. I left the invitation at my mother's house where they were planning to stay. The day before the party, my mother called me and said that Kevin wouldn't come but she would miss a dinner at her church and bring the children herself.

"You told me the guest speaker was a minister from Campbellford. That's why you didn't want to miss it in the first place. So why would you miss it now?"

My voice was harsh. I was annoyed with my mother for becoming involved in my dispute with Kevin.

"I can't talk anymore, Liz. They're right here." My mother's voice had dropped to a whisper. "I'll call you back later."

There was a loud click in my ear.

I immediately dialled my mother's number. The phone rang ten times without anyone answering. I hung up and dialled again, with the same result. I considered whether I should dial one more time. I knew it was unwise but I decided to drive to my mother's house and confront Kevin in person.

As I approached her street I saw Kevin's van parked in the driveway. My inner voice told me emphatically to turn around and go home but I was too irate to accept my own logic. I pulled into the driveway and parked behind the van.

I entered the house through the door in the garage. The sliding glass doors on the opposite side of the family room were open and I could see Kevin, Heather and their children sitting in the sun porch. The occasional clacking of crockery told me that my mother was washing dishes. As I started up the five steps leading to the kitchen, Kevin raised his head and looked at me. I kept moving.

My mother was standing at the sink with her hands immersed in soapy water. She was listening to a radio call-in show as she worked. I watched her rinse a bowl and place it on the draining rack.

"Why didn't you answer your phone?" I asked.

She looked around, startled.

"I didn't hear you come in," she said. She reached for a dirty plate without answering my question.

"I'm going to get Kevin and we'll settle this right now. He shouldn't be asking you to miss something you want to do just because he can't be bothered to bring Megan to the party."

I turned to go back to the family room. Kevin was standing at the bottom of the stairs.

"Fine. It's settled," he said. "She won't come."

His words were clipped and sharp, as if they had been shot from a gun. I knew Kevin hated messy arguments. I should have left it at that but I was angry and exhausted.

"You're such an asshole."

Kevin leaned one shoulder against the wall, his hands tucked in the front pockets of his jeans.

"I've told you before, Liz. I don't know what you expect from me."
His voice was flat.

"I just want you to act like my brother."

I moved down the stairs as I spoke, to distance our dispute from my mother. In the background, listeners were calling in to ask questions of an expert gardener.

Kevin began by outlining his complaints against me. He was calm and collected as he reviewed our history.

All I could do was cry as Kevin continued. At one point I tried to voice my own grievances, but the words were unintelligible through my tears.

The expert gardener continued to dispense advice. I wondered if my mother could hear our argument.

"Maybe you and Jeff and Heather and I should go out for dinner," Kevin concluded.

"Why would we do that?!"

I was still sobbing and could barely speak.

Later that evening, I told Jeff what Kevin had said. What I didn't disclose was that in addition to pointing out what he didn't like about me, Kevin had also acknowledged that he didn't like Jeff. I'm not sure whether I was trying to protect Jeff or Kevin by keeping that information secret. Perhaps I was trying to protect myself because somehow, that was the worst thing I had heard. I could convince myself that his comments about me were spoken in anger and that he didn't mean them. But everyone liked Jeff, so I could only wonder if Kevin disliked me so much that he also disliked anything and anyone associated with me.


BY THE SPRING of 2005, Kevin and I hadn't spoken for almost seven years. I could no longer ignore my mother's cognitive decline and knew that for her sake my brother and I would soon have to set aside our differences and try to work together.

My mother continued to obsess about the loss of her driver's license and was adamant that Dr. Kalansky's diagnosis was motivated by spite. Somewhere along the way, instead of referring to the doctor as *that Kalansky*, she became *your friend Kalansky*.

"Why is Dr. Kalansky suddenly my friend?" I asked one day in total frustration. "She's not my friend. She's not even my doctor."

"Well, you were the one that got me going to her in the first place, weren't you? She must be your friend," my mother said.

"I've told you a million times. I took you to see Dr. Kalansky eight years ago when you had pneumonia. You didn't have your own doctor because Dr. Nash had retired."

My mother snorted.

"Remember," I said, "it was the twenty-third of December and you were so sick. I had to take you somewhere. Dr. Kalansky was the only doctor I could find."

She shook her head.

"I'm sure I would remember if I had pneumonia."

"Mom, you stayed at my house for almost two weeks while I took care of you. And anyway, you've been going to see Dr. Kalansky yourself ever since. I haven't had anything to do with that."

"I didn't have a choice, did I?" she asked. "She's your friend. Of course I had to keep seeing her."

Neil's daughter, Sara, was getting married in July and my mother and I had both been invited to a bridal shower in her honour. By default, I was in charge of ensuring my mother's attendance.

My mother was sitting on the couch in her living room reading the Saturday edition of the *Winnipeg Free Press* when I arrived to pick her up for the event. She was dressed in the pink suit and silk blouse that we had set aside the day before. Instead of the cream leather pumps that we had chosen, she was wearing Nike running shoes. She frowned when she saw me standing in the front hall.

"I've changed my mind. I'm not going to this thing for Sara."

"What do you mean, Mom? You have to go to Sara's shower," I responded wearily. I knew what she was going to say next.

"If I can't drive myself to the shower, then I'm not going," my mother stated emphatically. "Anyway, I don't have a present for her so I can't go."

I assured my mother that the presents we had purchased together were wrapped and sitting in the back seat of my car. After fifteen minutes of cajoling, my mother finally grew tired of defending her position.

I pulled into the parking lot beside the church hall where the shower was being held and unbuckled my seatbelt. My mother sat motionless beside me. For a minute I was worried that she was going to refuse to get out of the car. We had only just arrived and I was already worn out, dreading the awkward small talk with women I didn't know, and worried that my mother wouldn't behave.

We dropped our gifts on a table piled high with brightly coloured boxes and bags. Several long wooden tables were set end to end in five parallel rows but we had arrived late and most of the seats were now filled. My mother and I were forced to sit near the back of the room, across from my nephew's girlfriend and her family. I had met the girl once before; my mother had not. We exchanged stiff hellos and they retreated to talking amongst themselves.

My mother's barrage of complaints began almost immediately.

*I don't know these people. Why didn't we bring a present? I can't see what's going on up there. No one told me Sara was getting married. I should have brought a present.*

As soon as I could, I made our excuses to Barb and Sara and hustled my mother out the door.

"Sara shouldn't even be having a wedding shower," my mother said when we were driving home. "She's been living with that guy she's marrying for years. But we should have brought her a present anyhow."

I wondered how she could remember that Sara and her boyfriend had been living together but she couldn't remember that we had brought presents for the shower.

"Mom, please," I said emphatically. "We DID bring presents."

She looked at me with doleful eyes.

"Do you think that doctor is right? Do you think I'm going simple?"

It had been a long afternoon and I didn't temper my response.

"Not simple – but there's no doubt that your memory is going."

My mother sat in sullen silence.

"Let's see what you're like when you're my age," she said finally.

By the end of June I was feeling increasingly worried about my mother's behaviour and overwhelmed with what might lay ahead. I knew that Kevin and his family would be coming to Winnipeg for Sara's wedding so I swallowed my pride and typed Kevin's name into my Google search bar. I found his email address on the website of the hospital where he was employed.

```
From:     "evmurray"
To:       "Kevin Murray"
Sent:     June 27, 2005  9:15 AM
Subject:  Mom

Kevin,
I'd like to get together to talk about my concerns about
Mom when you are in Winnipeg for Sara's wedding. I am
becoming increasingly concerned about her ability to
function appropriately. When would be a good time for us
to meet?
Liz
```

Kevin responded by suggesting that we could talk at the wedding reception. I had my doubts that a family gathering was the best spot for a serious exchange about my mother's ability to think logically and rationally but I would take what I could get.

The day of the wedding was unusually hot and humid, even for a Saturday in July. If there was air conditioning in the United Church, it wasn't sufficient to cool the sanctuary full of chattering guests. An usher escorted Jeff, Davis and me down the aisle and stopped at a pew reserved for the family of the bride. Kevin, Heather, and their children were already seated with my mother at the far end of the bench. Jeff deftly assumed the position closest to Kevin. We exchanged curt nods and then waited in silence for the first notes of the wedding processional.

After the ceremony, we filed outside to wait for the bride and groom to make their first appearance as a married couple. My mother surveyed the crowd from her position beside me at the bottom of the stairs leading into the church. She tugged on my arm and leaned over to whisper in my ear.

"Look at that man over there in the light suit!" she said. "He looks just like your father."

I looked in the direction she indicated. Kevin was having an animated discussion with a woman I didn't recognize.

"Do you mean the man talking to the woman in the blue dress?" I asked, hoping that I misunderstood the focus of my mother's attention.

She nodded.

"I just can't get over the likeness."

Since Kevin had escorted my mother to the wedding I was shocked that she didn't recognize her son. I maintained a breezy tone so she wouldn't become defensive about her mistake.

"Well, Mom, there's a good reason for that," I said with a half-hearted laugh. "That's Kevin."

My mother put her hand to her mouth. Her laugh was high pitched, more of a nervous giggle than a genuine laugh.

"Oooh you're right. He just looks different somehow."

The reception was held at a golf course on the outskirts of the city. A vaulted ceiling and large windows overlooking a green expanse provided an idyllic setting, but our table did little to contribute to the laughter and loud voices that filled the wood panelled room. I sat between my mother and Davis at our table for eight. Jeff again created a protective barrier in his chair beside Heather. Our conversation was polite but stilted and I welcomed the customary toasts and speeches to fill an uncomfortable void.

In the middle of the toast to the bride my mother nudged her chair closer to mine. She faced forward and spoke out of the side of her mouth like a character in a film noir spy movie.

"Who would have thought Sara had so much fun in her?"

I glared at her reprovingly. In the past, in an effort to control my father's affections, my mother had frequently attempted to recruit me as a soldier in her phantom war against Sara and her brother. One Christmas when Matthew was seven years old and Sara was almost ten, my mother launched a double offensive that was the ultimate example of her treacherous behaviour. Her first thrust was directed at Matthew, who was both victim and unwitting accomplice in the assault. We had just finished dinner and the children were excited about the gifts waiting for them under the tinsel-laden tree. My mother set out a large box of Pot of Gold chocolates on the coffee table while she waited for the family to assemble in the living room. As soon as Jeff removed the top of the box to study the flavour assortment guide, Matthew snatched a chocolate, popped it into his mouth and then grabbed a second and a third. His arms moved so quickly that it was difficult to know exactly how many candies he had managed to eat, but almost half the tray was empty and Matthew's cheeks had taken on the contour of a tennis ball. Barb entered the room just as her son opened his mouth to insert yet another Caramel Crème.

"Matthew, that's enough! You're going to be sick," she admonished. Her son's face had taken on an unhealthy sheen.

"Don't be silly," my mother retorted, her voice slightly taunting, her smile slightly cruel. "He can have a few more."

She sat in an armchair, one leg crossed over the other, swinging the bottom half of her top leg languidly, undaunted by the prospect of Mathew consuming candy until he vomited. She looked at me and winked. I responded by narrowing my eyes and pressing my lips into a quick frown. My mother commandeered the chocolate box and waved it enticingly in front of Matthew who had retreated to a chair in the corner, content to finish the candy stored in his cheeks. I glanced around the room to see if anyone else noticed her spiteful performance. Jeff winced as I caught his eye.

My mother's second strike of the evening was aimed at Sara who joined us in the kitchen to participate in the adult female ritual of washing the good china and silverware. Sara dutifully picked up a tea towel and positioned herself beside Barb, waiting for the first of the Crown Derby dinner plates to be rinsed. My mother tried to dissuade her with a brisk *Sara, you don't need to help* but Sara was oblivious to my mother's tone.

"That's okay, Grandma," she said. "I want to."

Unmoved by her granddaughter's enthusiasm, my mother pulled me aside and hissed, "I do not want THAT KID touching my dishes."

I was appalled by my mother's behavior even though I knew it came from her constant sense of insecurity.

When the wedding reception formalities ended, guests began to leave their seats to refresh their drinks at the bar or mingle with friends en route to the washrooms. Kevin stood up and walked quickly away from the table. He clearly didn't want to talk to me any more than I wanted to talk to him. I might not have pursued the matter if the incident at the church hadn't reignited my concern about my mother's failing memory.

I was finally able to corner Kevin at the edge of the dance floor. He wagged his head at my suggestion that we move to the lobby, and so I was forced to shout over the pounding beat of the Village People extolling the virtues of the YMCA. Neil joined us when I was halfway through a condensed version of the events that had occurred since Kevin's visit the previous summer.

Kevin stared at the couples squirming on the dance floor as I spoke. Neil made a sound that I interpreted to mean *she's crazy* instead of *she's ill*. I never thought that Neil was rude to my mother but I would often imagine a slight, and I would quietly take offence on her behalf, filing away the objectionable words as further evidence that she required my protection. I had become so accustomed to feeling defensive on my mother's behalf that I never stopped to consider whether it was warranted.

"Her cognitive functioning has definitely declined over the last year. And her paranoia has become worse," Kevin acknowledged after a brief silence. "I've arranged for her to be seen by a geriatric outpatient clinician."

I was both upset and relieved. Kevin's recognition of my mother's problems meant that they were real but I knew I needed more information on how to deal with her as she continued to decline.

"Let me know what the clinician has to say after the assessment. Call me at Victoria Beach, please. That's where I'll be."

The day after the assessment, I retrieved Kevin's message from my Winnipeg answering machine. He told me the clinician's name was Daryl Dyck and advised me how to reach him. He said the meeting went reasonably well but that my mother was resistant to Daryl's recommendations. Kevin did not offer details of the meeting or suggest that we should get together and talk about where we should go from here. Before I spoke to Daryl, I decided to call my mother and get her view of the assessment.

"Did you know that Kevin had someone here to read my head?" my mother demanded as soon as I said hello. "He thinks I'm crazy. And you were probably in on it too."

I wanted to point out how unlikely it was that Kevin and I would be collaborating on anything given our relationship, but she had already hung up on me.

I called Daryl Dyck and reached him on the third ring. He was understanding and gracious. He told me that he had conducted a basic memory and cognition test on my mother and confirmed that she was exhibiting symptoms of dementia. He told me there was no doubt that my mother was also demonstrating paranoid thought processes, but she was resistant to taking medication for a problem she didn't think she had. Since she was managing physically and wasn't prepared to admit to or accept help for her cognitive deficits, he said there was really nothing more he could do right now.

"It would be ideal if you could convince her to move out of her house," he suggested. "Sometimes we can't intervene until something bad happens like an accident or illness. It's unfortunate, but that's the way it is."

I appreciated Daryl's honesty, but waiting had never been my strong suit.

Several years earlier, my mother had told my friend Eleanor that she was worried about what I would do after she was gone. She never considered that she would be gone mentally but not physically. Caring for my mother had placed me on an emotional roller coaster, but what I didn't know then was that her mental health was about to become a runaway cart that no one would be able to stop.

Don't know why people hold spite against someone they really don't know - Kalansky was Liz's choice for me to go to

wish I'd never seen or heard tell of her -

~~seems she was always looking at anything she could use to say I was odd - everyone has their own way of thinking -~~

Kalansky is dangerous and often full of lies, never thought I'd run into anything like this

I love my daughter so much, just want her to

Kalansky said she would see to it that I never drove a car again.

Letter came from Kalansky saying I had early debenture.

Doesn't it seem odd this letter re unable to have license came around late November just when I was writing Xmas cards. Hadn't been to Kalansky since Aug. 5th. And what did I do to deserve this? Who has such spite?

Wanda Francey called me this morning and told me an elderly woman in her block got her drivers license this morning on a second try, she ~~could be seems to have trouble walking~~ hard of hearing but no one ever mentioned a medical to her, yet one of my notices said I would have to pay all expenses and have an examination at Health Science Centre before getting my license

Kalansky was someone Liz had me see, think she and Liz are friends - she started some conversation I wasn't even interested in - in that conversation she mentioned a number lets say "182" and then asked me what the number was. I just said I don't remember but this problem started about then. After I had a blood test. I waited around outside - debating if I should go back in and wait to see what she had to say, but I thought I was finished with her for the day as she hadn't told me to return to her office - and it was such a beautiful day, wanted to get the lawn cut etc. at home, so came home Anyhow about 10 AM the next morning she called me and said re: not reporting back to her and be down there by 3:30 pm - went down and asked her (guess I apologized) why she wanted to see me - her reply was something like "nothing, you can go now." Felt like a school child - can still see the smirk or smile on her face.

Wanda Francey had another car accident yesterday - that's at least 4 this past year. She cut in front of a truck after passing it and didn't notice another car. Made a mess of her fender - she brought it over to show to me. Will probably cost a lot to fix as garages really charge when they can

# Chapter Eleven

**I HAD BEEN** calling my mother from our cottage at Victoria Beach without success since Sunday morning. It wasn't unusual for her to refuse to answer the phone for days at a time and I had learned not to ask why she hadn't been answering. Her standard reply was *why do you want to know or what difference does it make?*

I tried her number one more time.

"Hey Mom, how're you doing?"

She told me that Marion Fleming, an old friend who lived in Toronto, had stopped by for a visit. My mother's voice was animated and she spoke just slightly faster than was normal.

"It's so nice to see Marion. I told her all about Kalansky and my driver's license. She couldn't believe it. She said there was no reason why I shouldn't be driving."

"What's Marion's news?" I asked, wanting to change the subject.

"She's right here," my mother said, her tone triumphant. "You can ask her yourself."

I could hear my mother say that I was on the line as she passed the phone to her friend.

"Hi, Mrs. Fleming, how are you?"

She told me that one of her daughters had just returned from a vacation in Italy and another was going through a difficult divorce. I updated her with information about Davis and Jeff.

"Your mom has been telling me how she lost her driver's license," Marion said eventually. I heard my mother snort in the background. Marion's voice was cheerful but she seemed to be choosing her words carefully.

"I'm trying to tell her that she should stop worrying about it so much."

Marion paused.

"Your mother's just gone to the washroom." She lowered her voice. "Liz, I don't think she's well at all. I mean, she seems okay physically, but – I couldn't reach her on the telephone so I just stopped by. She thought I'd been spying on her. And this business about her driver's license –"

"Oh, Mrs. Fleming," I blurted, "I just don't know what to do about her."


ON THE SATURDAY of the long weekend in August, Jeff was sitting in an Adirondack chair on the front deck of our cottage when I returned from the bakery with a loaf of still warm sourdough bread.

"Your mother called," he said, motioning for me to sit in the chair next to his. "She changed her mind. She wants to come to the cottage after all."

I was unenthusiastic. Jeff and I had been in the city the day before and my mother had declined our invitation to visit. I didn't want to waste another beautiful day at the cottage driving back into Winnipeg.

"I said you'd talk to her as soon as you got back," Jeff told me.

I called my mother and told her I would be happy to come and pick her up. She should be ready by eleven o'clock, I told her, hoping that she would be ready by noon when I expected to arrive. All she had to do was pack a bag.

When I pulled up to my mother's house she was cutting the front lawn. She waved.

"I'm almost done," she shouted over the sound of the mower.

I sat on the front steps, watching her push the mower up, across, and down the lawn with regimental precision. My mother had always enjoyed yard work but now she was zealous about keeping the grass cut. In the spring when Jeff had offered to help, my mother was resolute in her refusal.

"Just because I can't drive a car doesn't mean I can't use a lawn mower," she had told him.

I leaned back on my elbows and stretched my legs. At least two-thirds of the lawn was untouched. It was going to be a long wait.

It was past one o'clock when she pushed the lawn mower into the garage and coiled the extension cord into a loose circle. The cord was held together with black electrician's tape in more than half a dozen places. Each black mark represented a time when my mother had run over the cord with the mower. Two years ago, Jeff had bought her a new cord and suggested that the old one was no longer safe to use. The purchase, still in its original packaging, was sitting idle on a shelf next to the garden supplies.

"Are you all packed, Mom? It's such a beautiful day. We should be at the beach." I had joined my mother in the garage, hoping to hurry her along.

"I'll just go pack now," she said. "Come and tell me what I should bring."

I followed her into the bedroom, watching her rummage aimlessly in a drawer and then in her closet.

"I just don't know where all my things go. I can never find anything when I want it."

"Why don't I put some things together while you get your toiletries?" I suggested impatiently.

"First I need to find the number for the *Free Press*. I'd better cancel the paper if I'm going to your cottage for a couple of weeks."

I didn't dare question the duration of her visit.

"I'll call the paper, Mom. You get your toiletries together."


It was almost six o'clock when we arrived at Victoria Beach. During July and August, cars are prohibited in the main cottage area and residents and visitors must leave their vehicles in the large parking lot at the entrance to the community. A fleet of old station wagons acts as a taxi service but most people walk or ride a bicycle wherever they want to go.

"Do you want to walk or take a taxi, Mom?"

The sides of her mouth turned down. Her eyes were clouded when she looked at me. I had reviewed the no car rule with her on the drive but she had either forgotten or had not understood what I said.

The next morning, we decided to walk to the old wooden building that housed the bakery. The enticing aroma of vanilla, cinnamon and cloves hung over the pastry cases like a hypnotic cloud, propelling us toward the rows of fresh cinnamon buns, pecan loaves, apple turnovers, and Eccles cakes. My mother had a weakness for sticky buns and looked as if she were in heaven.

Bakery bag in hand, we started back to the cottage. I pointed out the tree-lined gravel roads that look like country lanes in a little English village. I showed her the tennis courts where Davis and his friends spent hours of their time, and the sports field where annual soccer, baseball, and volleyball tournaments were held. We walked past the clubhouse that hosted the flea market, yoga classes and movie nights for children.

"It's very nice here, Liz," my mother said, "but don't you miss being on the water? Why don't you sell this place and come back to Falcon Lake?"

"I'm sorry, Mom," I said. "I've told you, we really like it here. It's the perfect place for us."

I took her hand and squeezed gently. She kept her head facing forward and her eyes on the road ahead. I smiled at her even though she wasn't looking at me, hoping she would notice out of the corner of her eye.

"You know you're always welcome to come and stay with us."

"I want to go to my own cottage. And now that I can't drive, I can't go."

Her voice trembled as she spoke. She still wouldn't look at me. We were quiet as we continued our walk home.

That afternoon, I suggested that my mother might like to watch Davis and his buddies tubing at the pier. My mother looked up from the driver's handbook she had insisted on packing. I had been helping her study for ten months and she still hadn't written the test.

"I haven't been doing much studying lately, so I should really stay and do my work," she said. "But I would like to watch Davis."

"It takes me time to get the Sea-Doo set up. Why don't you study for a few more minutes, and then in half an hour or so, you and Jeff can walk down to the pier and see what we're doing."

When I saw Jeff and my mother setting up lawn chairs on the cement jetty, I waved and shouted a greeting as they settled into their chairs to watch the boys take turns being pulled behind the watercraft.

After dinner we sat in the screened porch enjoying the last remnants of the warm summer day. Sunburned and satisfied, my mother seemed like the old Mamie for the first time since she had lost her driver's license.

"I think I should go home tomorrow," my mother said suddenly. "I'm worried about the house. You never know if those neighbours are going to be emptying their cesspool into my backyard when I'm gone."

For the past few years my mother had been worried about the water that accumulated in her backyard in the spring and after a heavy rainfall. Her property was much lower than any of the surrounding yards but she was adamant that the excess moisture was caused by her neighbours siphoning the contents of their above ground pool onto her property. She had recently become convinced that a hidden septic field was adding to the problem.

Jeff looked at me. His head and shoulders sagged into a not this again look.

"I don't think you have to worry about that, Mother-in-law," he said affectionately. "Stay another day and enjoy yourself."

"You don't know what those people are like." She lifted her mug of tea to her mouth, but lowered it again without taking a sip. "I need to be there to make sure they're not up to something."

My mother was carrying her suitcase when she finally came out of her bedroom the next morning.

"I'll just put this in the car," she said, walking towards the front door.

"Whoa, Mom, where're you going?" I got out of my chair and took her suitcase from her hand. "The car isn't here, remember?"

"What do you mean? Where is it then?" She shifted her position so she could study the space in front of the cottage from the window. "Did someone take it?" She turned back to me with a frown.

"It's in the parking lot. No cars allowed at Victoria Beach, remember?"

The pitch of my voice was a little higher than usual.

"How did we get here, then?"

She looked out the front window again and narrowed her eyes.

Jeff cleared his throat. When I looked at him, he pressed his lips together and shook his head slightly.

"Why don't you come and sit down, Mother-in-law." Jeff stood up and pulled the chair beside his out from the table. "Have some breakfast. I'll drive you home after you eat."

My mother's eyes moved from my face to Jeff's and back to mine. Her shoulders were tense. Jeff motioned again to the chair.

"I've made coffee for you. And we have some pecan loaf from yesterday."

He was doing his best to divert my mother's attention away from the things that she couldn't remember.

"Good idea," I said, mimicking his strategy.

I put my mother's suitcase by the door and moved closer to the table. She hesitated a moment longer before reluctantly accepting a cup of coffee.

"Your mother is getting worse," Jeff said matter-of-factly when he returned to the cottage later that evening.

If she had been less defensive my mother and I could have discussed her problems but she had never been prepared to acknowledge her weaknesses. She wasn't going to change now. I pushed my concerns to the back of my mind but as the summer progressed, she became increasingly paranoid and erratic.


"YOUR FRIEND KALANSKY has made sure that I can't see Dr. Wong anymore," my mother told me one day. Dr. Turnley Wong was an internist who for the last ten years had been monitoring the chronically low platelets in my mother's blood.

"What are you talking about? Why would Dr. Kalansky do that?"

I still struggled to find the logic in my mother's pronouncements.

"Because she hates me, that's why. She sent Dr. Wong a copy of her letter that said I'm crazy and now he doesn't want to have anything to do with me."

"Maybe it's standard practice for a doctor to send those reports to all of a patient's other physicians," I offered, more as an explanation to myself than to her. "My oncologist sends an update to my family doctor all the time. I'm sure Dr. Wong isn't going to refuse to see you."

"There you go taking Kalansky's side again. And don't tell me what Dr. Wong is going to do. You weren't there."

My mother terminated our conversation with a loud click.

A few days later when I dropped by to ease the tension, a strange car was in the driveway.

"Hi Mom, it's me," I called, as I opened the screen door.

I could hear her talking to someone in the kitchen but I couldn't distinguish the deeper, male voice. The room's pocket door was half closed. My mother squeezed through the opening and met me in the living room.

"Oh, it's you," she said. She stood for a second with her arms crossed and looked at me. She wasn't smiling.

"Hi, Mom," I said again. "I just thought I'd stop by for a quick visit."

She stood looking at me for another second.

"Well, I guess you'd better come in then."

She slid the door open and returned to the kitchen, leaving me to trail behind. I hesitated, wondering if I should come back another time.

One of the ministers from my mother's church was getting to his feet to greet me. Father Henry was tall with broad shoulders and thick muscular arms. When he cupped one of my hands in both of his, it was a hand hold rather than a handshake.

"Hello, Elizabeth. It's so nice to see you. Come, sit down and visit with us," he urged, his Jamaican patois accent transforming all of his words into a song.

My mother had resumed her seat and was staring at her hands clasped in front of her. Father Henry either didn't notice her lack of enthusiasm or chose to ignore her apathy.

I moved behind my mother's chair to the empty seat beside her. She tensed when I touched her shoulder lightly as I passed.

"And how is little Davis?" Father Henry asked. Davis had been only two

years old when he first met Father Henry, and ever since, Father Henry had
called him Little Davis.

"Davis is okay, I guess," I said tentatively, looking for a reaction from my
mother. She didn't look up, even when I mentioned Davis' name. "He's just
starting hockey try-outs, and he's a little nervous."

My mother shifted in her chair to face Father Henry and turn her back to
me. Her arms and legs were both crossed.

"How is that new priest doing, Father Henry? I haven't had a chance to
get to know him," she interjected.

"Oh, Mamie, you know how it is with our congregation. Some people
are happy and some are not." He chuckled a little. "I just try to mind my own
business and do my job."

My mother was not deterred by his tactful response.

"Who's not happy?" She stopped and glowered at me. "Now that I can't
drive, I have to go to the ten o'clock service with Wanda Francey. I don't see
any of my old friends."

"Mamie, Mamie," Father Henry chuckled again, and then turned his
attention back to me. "Tell me about these hockey try-outs Little Davis is
worrying about."

"Well," I said, "Davis is trying out for a team that he should have made
last year but didn't. So he's feeling a lot of pressure." I shook my head. "He was
really upset last year. We're a little worried about him."

I looked at my mother. Usually the news that Davis was or had been
upset for any reason was enough to make her upset too. Today she remained
impassive.

"How is Mrs. Talbot doing?" she asked abruptly. "I hear she's been sick."

I knew my mother had been feeling disconnected from her church
community since she had lost her driver's license but I was still baffled by her
curt attitude. After a few more minutes of awkward conversation, I decided
to leave and let her have Father Henry to herself.

My mother's attitude remained blustery but one day when I thought she was in a friendlier mood I asked if she would shorten two pairs of pants for Davis. She happily agreed so I told her that I would drop the pants off that afternoon. As I approached the driveway, I could see my mother watering the plants she kept in front of the living room window. I honked my horn and waved. My mother looked up but didn't wave back. She watched as I parked my car and started walking towards the house.

When I opened the front door, my mother was standing in the hallway, still holding her watering can.

"What do you want?"

Her voice sounded hard and cold. I stepped inside, and then stood still as she moved closer to the door. She brandished her watering can like a sword, blocking my entry. For a second I was speechless.

"What do you mean?"

I took a step backwards and involuntarily lifted Davis' pants to my chest for protection.

"You know what I mean, Elizabeth." Her eyes were as hard and cold as her voice. "You've played all those dirty tricks on me. What do you want to do to me this time?"

The watering can was by her side now, but she waved it a little as she spoke.

"Mom, I – I really don't know what you're talking about. I –"

"Oh, you know, Elizabeth," she interrupted. "Don't play dumb with me."

I had no idea what my mother had decided I had done but I was getting angry in response to her accusations. I took a deep breath and forced myself to stay calm.

"Mom, I've just come for a visit and to bring you Davis' school pants to shorten."

"I don't want to visit with you." Her eyes were steely. "I just want you to leave."

I remained motionless. I didn't believe what I was hearing.

"You can take Davis' pants with you."

She put her free hand on the front door and started to swing it closed, despite the fact that I stood in the way.

By the time I arrived home, there were three telephone messages from my mother on my answering machine. In the first, her voice was still hard. She said she had changed her mind and would shorten Davis' pants if I brought them back. In the second, she sounded teary. She said she was sorry; she didn't know what had come over her. Would I please come back? And bring Davis' pants. By the third, she was crying.

"Please Liz," she said, "I didn't mean it. Please come back right away."

My mother was sitting at the kitchen table when I arrived. Her eyes were swollen and her cheeks and forehead were covered in red blotches. My face often looked the same way after I had been crying. I knelt on the floor beside her chair and put my arms around her. She wiped her nose with a soggy tissue and rested her head against mine.

"I'm sorry, Liz," she said finally. "I'm so sorry." Her eyes welled up with tears.

"Mom, it's okay. Don't cry anymore. It's okay."

I rubbed her back slowly and made shushing sounds. She took a long, shaky breath.

"I don't know what came over me." Her voice quivered and she took another shaky breath. "I just don't know what's happening to me." Her face crumpled.

"Okay, okay."

I kept rubbing her back and making soft cooing sounds as if she was a distressed infant. I didn't know what else to do except start crying myself.

When my mother was finally calmed, I pushed myself off the floor and onto a chair.

"Hey, I brought you Davis' pants," I said brightly. "Do you think you have time to shorten them for me?"

She reached out and touched the pants.

"Of course I do," she said. "When don't I have time for Davis?"

Three days later, I was making scrambled eggs for breakfast when the phone rang.

"I know you wanted me to do something with these pants, Liz, but I just can't think what."

My mother had started talking even before I could say hello.

"No problem, Mom. You just need to make the longer pants the same as the shorter ones."

I had left my mother with the new pair of pants that needed hemming as well as an old pair to use as a guide. It was something she had done many times and I had reviewed the job with her just to be sure.

"But they look the same to me," she said. She sounded uncertain. "They're both grey wool pants. Are you sure you left the right ones?"

I agreed, impatiently, that yes, they were the same pants. One pair just needed to be shortened.

"Just a minute, let me look." My mother dropped the phone. When she came back she sounded relieved. "That's all right, then. I've figured it out now." She laughed a little. "I'm so stupid sometimes."

She called again on the weekend.

"You know those pants you left me? Who do they belong to? I couldn't remember, so I tried them on. They fit me, so they can't belong to Davis." My mother's voice was smug. "I think you've made a mistake this time."

"No, they're his. The kids wear their pants baggy these days. That's the style."

My mother was not ready to give up. "Well, okay, I'm happy to fix them but they look far too big for Davis."

By Monday, her mood had changed again.

"Elizabeth, can you please come and get these pants," my mother said in her telephone message. "I need them out of my way."

The front door was open when I arrived but there was no sign of my mother on the main floor.

"Mom?" I called.

"Who's there?" My mother came down the stairs. Her hair was set in pink foam curlers. "Oh, it's you." Her voice was contemptuous. "Your pants are in there."

She waved towards the dining room where the pants were sitting on one end of the table, neatly folded.

"Thanks for doing this, Mom. I really appreciate it," I said.

"I didn't do it for you. I did it for Davis." She turned her back to me. "But I won't do it again. So don't ask me."

"Mom, what's going on here?" I shook my head in exasperation even though she couldn't see me. "Why are you so angry with me all of a sudden?"

I followed my mother into the kitchen and watched her pull out a large mixing bowl and a bag of flour. She deliberately kept her back to me as she worked.

"Well, let's just say I've found out what you've been up to."

She moved to the refrigerator and removed a carton of eggs.

"I had a hunch you were involved in this driver's license business, and now I know for sure. You and your friend Kalansky."

I sat down at the table and rested my chin on my hand.

"Mom, I don't know what to say to you." I took a deep breath. "Dr. Kalansky is not my friend. And I had nothing to do with you losing your driver's license."

My mother had cracked three eggs into the bowl and was beating them furiously with a fork.

I sat in silence and watched my mother work. When I couldn't stand it any longer, I tried again.

"Mom, it's Thanksgiving weekend. We're going to the cottage for Saturday and Sunday. So I thought I'd make Thanksgiving dinner on Monday. Is that okay with you?"

"Have it whenever you want," my mother said. "I'm not coming."

On Thanksgiving Monday, the ringing telephone was abruptly disconnected as I pushed open the door from the garage, and keyed in our alarm code. It was four o'clock in the afternoon and Davis and I were just arriving home from Victoria Beach, with Jeff still to come in his own vehicle. I had a car full of dirty laundry, suitcases and groceries to unload but first I needed to see if the caller had left a message. Since my conversation with Daryl Dyck, the geriatric clinician who had examined my mother in the summer, I was always afraid that I would miss a call alerting me to a crisis with my mother. That fear had become a Pavlovian response to the red light on our telephone that signalled missed calls.

Call display confirmed that my mother had tried to contact me six times, but there was no message.

"Hi Mom, I just missed you," I said, when my mother picked up after just one ring.

"How do you know I called?" Her tone was aggressive.

I had explained the wonders of call display several times but since my mother had not moved past her rotary dial, the concept had always been beyond her grasp.

"Just a lucky guess, I suppose. What's up?"

"Oh, yes." She sounded more hesitant now, as if she was trying to remember why she had called in the first place. "I was wondering if I could still come over for dinner tonight. For Thanksgiving."

"Mom, I'm so sorry. You said you wouldn't come, so we decided to stay longer at the cottage. I just got in the door. I'm not making dinner tonight."

I had renewed my invitation three times the preceding week and each time my mother had refused. When we made the decision to stay another night at the cottage, I had thought it would serve my mother right if she changed her mind at the last minute. Now I felt guilty.

"How about tomorrow night instead?" I asked. "I'll pick you up when I pick up Davis from school."

Jeff arrived home just as I was saying goodbye.

"My mother," I told him in response to his mouthed who is it?

He smiled. "Let me guess."

I was in the kitchen mashing potatoes and stirring gravy while we waited for Jeff to come home from work for our belated Thanksgiving dinner.

"Let's get these pots and pans washed up before we eat," my mother suggested.

"Don't worry about it," I told her. "They'll just go in the dishwasher."

She stared blankly at the black door of the appliance by the sink.

"When did you get one of those contraptions?"

"Oh, quite a while ago," I replied vaguely. We had always had a dishwasher. "Why don't you relax until dinner?"

My mother moved into the family room and pulled out her driver's handbook. Davis was sitting in the chair beside her watching sports highlights on TSN. Every few minutes she would read out loud from the handbook.

"When you learn how to drive, Davis, remember that you have to slow down when you pass a school bus," she told him.

"If you don't write that test soon, Mom, you and Davis will be doing it together," I teased, hoping she would take the hint that she should either write the test or forget about it.

"You know, I was just thinking I should do it one day this week." She bit her lip and laughed nervously. "Do you think I'm ready?"

This wasn't the first time my mother had decided to write the test one day this week. I didn't feel right encouraging her to write the test when I was confident that she wouldn't pass but it was safer than me telling her not to.

"As ready as you'll ever be. All you can do is give it a try."

My mother nodded and turned her attention back to the handbook. She looked like a four-year-old trying to puzzle through the words of a Dr. Seuss book. I fought an urge to hug her tight and never let her go.

"Dinner is delicious, Liz, I'm so glad you convinced me to come."

My mother's plate held generous portions of turkey, mashed potatoes, steamed broccoli and salad. It was more food than she normally ate in a week.

"We're glad you decided to join us," Jeff said. "You know, you could come over for dinner more often. Why don't you give some thought to selling your house and moving closer to us?"

Jeff and I had been discussing that possibility since the summer when Daryl Dyck had made a similar recommendation. I knew my mother wouldn't view the suggestion favourably so I hadn't had the courage to initiate the discussion with her. I looked at Jeff and opened my eyes wide, hoping to discourage him from pursuing the topic.

My mother's fork, loaded with turkey, was halfway to her mouth. She returned it to her plate and looked at Jeff. The lines in her forehead became deeper as she drew her eyebrows together.

"Why would I do that?" she asked. "I'm going to write my driver's test and then I'll be fine staying right where I am. In my own house."

"That's great, Mother-in-law. If you get your driver's license back. But let's say for a minute that you don't; what do you think you should do then?"

Jeff's voice was deliberately casual. He took a sip of water and looked at my mother over the rim of his glass. "Maybe it's time we started talking about a contingency plan."

"I have a plan. My plan is to move back to Ontario."

My mother's pale blue eyes had darkened to navy.

For as long as I could remember, whenever my mother was unhappy about her life in Winnipeg, she would say she was moving back to Ontario. She often told me that when I was two years old she had the car packed and ready to go but I clung to my father and wouldn't leave. Her words had always angered me. I considered them a rejection of her life in Winnipeg – the life that included me.

Since my father's death, moving back to Ontario was her threat whenever I refused to follow her wishes. When Jeff and I were looking for a larger home before we had decided to build, my mother wanted us to buy the house two doors down from her. If we didn't buy that house, she said, she was moving back to Ontario.

"Oh, come on, Mom, that's not going to happen. You know that!" I sputtered across the table.

"Why isn't it going to happen?" my mother demanded. "I'm going to get my driver's license back, and then I'm moving to Ontario. I've been thinking about it for a while now."

She sat back in her chair and crossed her arms. She tilted her chin slightly and glared, first at the head of the table where I was sitting and then across the table at Jeff.

"That's ridiculous. You're eighty-four-years old. Why would you move –"

"That's fine, Mother-in-law," Jeff soothed. "But that still assumes you get your driver's license back. What if you don't? I'm just suggesting that maybe it's time for us to talk about options in case that's the way it goes."

My mother pushed her chair back and stood up from the table.

"It's time for me to go home," she said as she walked toward the back hall. We heard the closet door open and close, followed by a couple of soft thuds that told us she was putting on her shoes. "Liz, I want to go home now," she repeated loudly.

Jeff and I looked at each other. He moved his hand up and down slowly, palm facing downwards; his signal for me to calm down. I pressed my lips together tightly so I wouldn't yell, and counted to twelve – ten wasn't high enough.

"Mom, please sit down and finish dinner, and then I'll drive you home if you want," I finally managed to say dispassionately.

"No, Elizabeth, I'm going home now. If you won't drive me, I'll just have to walk."

The alarm beep signalled that my mother had opened the door to the garage.

As I pulled out of the driveway, my mother twisted her body so she was looking out the passenger window with the back of her shoulders facing me.

"Look, Mom, we're just trying to get you to consider some realistic alternatives. That's all, we're not –"

"It's all because of you and your pal Kalansky. You never should have made me see that woman."

"Mom, she's not my pal."

"I'm not talking about this with you anymore, Elizabeth. I'm moving to Ontario, and that's that," she said. "If I don't get my driver's license back in Winnipeg, I'll get it in Ontario."

"You'll have to write a test in Ontario, too," I told her. "It's not going to be any different there."

"Oh, yes, it will," she said. "Your friend Kalansky's not in Ontario. She's probably fixed it so I couldn't pass that test here even if I tried."

"That's just crazy. You're not making any sense." I spoke emphatically.

She turned her head and gave me a cold look. In that moment, I wished she would move to Ontario.

Was at Liz and Jeff's cottage at Victoria Beach. I went for two weeks but just stayed for one week. Jeff drove me back. There was one incident that was supposed to make me feel uncomfortable. Jeff asked me to go down to the beach with him - then a little while later we saw Liz with Davis and some of his friends sitting on another part of the beach just down from us. I could see them quite clearly but they weren't within speaking distance - they were laughing and talking and every once in a while they would point at Jeff and I. The kids were in and out of the water. Liz didn't come over and talk to me. Jeff eventually went over to them and I was alone until he came back.

called Kalansky's office
979 4060

asked to have my
medical record sent over
to Dr. Turnley Wong
St. Boniface General office Hospital
409 Tache Avenue
Wpg. Man
R2H 2A6

All my records from Kalansky
were sent over to Dr Wong. I
didn't realize it wasn't Kalansky
that sent all my appointments over
to him - the last time I went he
received this telephone call and
he asked me to wait until he got
back from checking his mail box
- when he got back he handed me a
file of the number of times I had
been to Kalansky - Liz got me going
to her and for awhile I was going
to them both

THIS WAS LIZ WHO SENT
RECORDS OVER TO DR. WONG NOT
KALANSKY (I never had any idea
just what she was up to)

KEEP FOR TRIAL RE LIZ

DR WONG   RE KALANSKY

HAD APPOINTMENT

  WITH  DR. WONG

  AFTER EXAMINATION HE TOLD

  ME  KALANSKY HAD SENT OVER

ALL THE PAPERS SHE HAD RE MY HEALTH.

HE SEEMED TO CHANGE HIS

DISPOSITION TOWARD ME

THEN AND HANDED ME

  ALL THE PAPERS —

  HE USUALLY MADE

  ANOTHER APPOINTMENT WITH

ME, BUT THIS TIME NEVER

MENTIONED ONE — INSTEAD

BROUGHT UP KALANSKYS

NAME

SOUNDED RATHER DISGUSTED

  WITH ME —

  DON'T KNOW IF HE KNEW

  BEFORE THEN THAT I WAS

GOING TO HER, I KNOW

I NEVER TOLD HIM.

DO NOT DESTROY

HUNG ON TIGHTLY TO PAPERS
ALL THE WAY HOME ON THE
BUS — WENT INTO STORE
AT GAS STATION
I WAS FEELING A BIT UPSET AT
HIS MANNER AND THE WHOLE
THING, GOT BREAD AND
MILK FROM STORE AND I
KNOW I HAD PAPERS WITH
ME WHEN I WENT TO THE
COUNTER BUT CAME AWAY
WITHOUT THEM — WENT BACK
TO STORE, SPOKE WITH
MANAGER — HE SAID THEY
DIDN'T HAVE LARGE ENVELOPE
WITH MY NAME ON OUTSIDE— THINK
HE KNEW SOMETHING
ABOUT THEM BUT
INSISTED NO PAPERS HAD BEEN LEFT
WENT UP TUESDAY MORNING
AGAIN TO CHECK AT GARAGE
STORE, BUT MANAGER STILL
SAID HE HADN'T SEEN
ANY PAPERS TURNED IN —
LOOKED AS THOUGH HE WAS LYING AND KNEW ALL
ABOUT THEM

WAS TELLING HENRY ABOUT ALL THE
GOINGS ON WITH TURNLEY & KALANSKY
PLUS CAR LICENSE LOST — LIZ WHO
NEVER COMES OVER JUST HAPPENED TO DROP BY
ANYHOW SHE LEFT — HAVEN'T HEARD FROM HER SINCE
SHE IS STILL ANGRY BECAUSE I WOULDN'T TURN THE
COTTAGE OVER TO HER

Liz came wed to pick up a pair of pants I had
shortened for Davis – then went back to her place
for supper – all through supper I felt there was
a lot of tension in the air –
Davis had to go do his homework upstairs –
shortly after something came up about how
Liz looked after me at her place when I had
pneumonia – the conversation ended when somehow
she brought in that Kalansky was the doctor she
brought in to look after me
Liz thought i should have remembered all about it.
I remember being ill at her place – in bed for
maybe a week or so – (how can I remember all
the details when I was sick and slept or maybe
was unconscious a lot of the time)
Then the drivers license was mentioned and Liz
mentioned I would never drive a car again. I said
I may move east and she said I wouldn't get a
license there either – now I never had an accident
– only one complaint and that was a couple years
ago when I was speeding one Sunday morning as
I was late for church
Anyway since then Liz has reported me as
having a poor memory

# Chapter Twelve

WHEN I WAS a teenager, my quarrels with my mother could be ugly but they never lasted long. My mother would take my insults to heart and succumb to tears long before I was ready to call a truce.

"I've done my best for you but you've always hated me," she would sob.

Sometimes her tears made me angrier. More often, I felt guilty that I had the power to hurt her so badly and ashamed that I had abused my power so readily. I was usually the first to apologize and ask for forgiveness, which she would grant with open arms. We would then carry on as if our argument had never happened. Ultimately, each of us had known that we could count on the other's unconditional love.

Since my mother's premature departure from our Thanksgiving dinner, our communication had been sparse and unpleasant. She now claimed that Dr. Kalansky had diagnosed her with dementia on my instruction so that I could *get back at her* for some reason that she wouldn't articulate. When she requested a ride to and from Holy Trinity Anglican Church for the monthly meeting of the Altar Guild, I hoped that it was a sign her hostility towards me had disappeared as quickly as it had appeared.

I did most of the talking as I drove her to the church. I updated her with news of Davis' success on a math test and told her about an upcoming school dance – information that she typically collected with the zeal of a dedicated philatelist. She listened politely but didn't respond.

On the ride home her attitude was cold and vacant. She leaned slightly forward in her seat with her chin raised and her shoulders rigid, maintaining an inch of space between her body and the seat back; she pressed her feet firmly into the floorboard so that her legs formed a perfect right angle at her knees. All of my attempts at conversation were flatly rejected. As we approached her house I made a last effort at appeasement.

"I'm just making arrangements for your snow removal, Mom. Any special instructions?"

Every year she complained that the work didn't comply with her specifications.

"I don't want you doing anything for me. You've done enough by taking away my driver's license," she snapped.

She hopped out, slamming the door behind her, and marched purposefully back down the driveway to the street. I watched in the rear view mirror as she made a sharp right turn.

"Mom, where are you going?" I called out, with one foot on the driveway and the other on the brake. She dismissed me with a backward flick of her wrist and continued her march up the street.

The evening was warm. The neighbourhood was safe. I started the car and drove home.

When I stopped by her house a few days later, the door was locked and she didn't answer when I rang the doorbell. I tried to open the front door with my key but it wouldn't turn in the lock.

I returned home and called my mother.

"Hey, Mom," I said. "I was just at your place and my key wouldn't work in the front door. Did you change the lock? "

"Yes, I did," she replied flatly.

"Why? Did you lose your key? "

"No," she said, again without offering a fuller explanation.

"Then why?" I persisted, pushing down the queasy feeling in my stomach.

"I have my reasons."

Her voice sounded triumphant now.

"Well, are you going to give me a copy of the new key? Just in case of an emergency?"

"No, Elizabeth, I'm not. I don't want you to have a key to my house anymore. "

I had had my own key to the house since I was ten years old. I was astounded that she would now refuse me entry.

In the past, my mother might have remained angry with me for one or two days but something was definitely different. I knew she wouldn't agree to see Dr. Kalansky so I decided to contact Daryl Dyck. Daryl had advised me that his role as an outpatient clinician was to connect seniors with appropriate resources rather than to develop ongoing relationships but I was hopeful that he would visit my mother again. After I explained my concerns, he agreed to my request.

In the interim, I resolved to email Kevin and ask him for assistance. Since Dr. Wong and Kevin were acquainted through the medical community, I thought my brother could ask him for information about what had happened at my mother's last appointment. I hoped that Kevin could provide insight into what was motivating her current behaviour but secretly I was wishing that she was treating him as badly as she was treating me.

```
From:      "evmurray"
To:        "Kevin Murray"
Sent:      November 4, 2005 1:06 PM
Subject:   Re: mom

Kevin,
What kind of contact are you having with Mom lately? She
has been very angry with me for the past several weeks.
I'm not sure what sparked her off, but she blames me for
everything that is bad with her life. She hangs up on me
when I telephone her and tells me to leave if I go over.
I haven't been pushing it — just trying to check in with
her on the phone a couple of times a week — but it's not
getting any better. I am very worried about her mental
state and don't know what to do. What do you think?
I'm wondering if you could call Turnley Wong and ask
him what happened at their last appointment. That's when
things started to disintegrate. She has ranted about Dr.
K sending Dr. Wong copies of her records and how wrong
that was etc. She said she wouldn't see him again, but I
don't know if she meant it. Would you please speak to him
and let me know what happened? I thought he might be more
candid with you about her status.
Liz
```

Kevin's return email was brief. He said that in their recent telephone conversations, my mother had been angry with me. She complained to him that at Thanksgiving dinner I had told her she would never drive again, and that I was part of a conspiracy to prevent her from ever regaining her license. His response only added to my feeling of helplessness.

Daryl Dyck called me back two weeks later and confirmed that he had been to see my mother. When he arrived, my mother had forgotten she had agreed to see him and denied that she had met him before. Daryl convinced her to let him in the house and she was soon happy to discuss her problems. He reported that she was unusually hostile towards me and that her paranoia seemed to be more extreme than it had been just a few months before.

"It might be useful," he said, "for you to contact the Alzheimer's Society and join a support group. Your mother's case is atypical – at least initially, she appears much more functional than she really is – but she clearly has symptoms of the disease."

I listened as he explained some of the differences between normal aging and dementia. "For example," he said, "misplacing a name is normal; forgetting a familiar face is not."

His words struck a nerve. In the fall of 2001, my mother had telephoned me as soon as she arrived home from church.

"You'll never guess who was helping with Communion today," she said.

"Who?" I dutifully replied.

"Janet Buhr," my mother responded enthusiastically. "I didn't recognize her even after she told me her name."

"How could you not have recognized Janet Buhr?" I asked, unable to hide my astonishment.

I met Janet Buhr and her sister, Mary Anne, when I was seven years old. We all attended Sunday School at Holy Trinity Anglican Church. The three of us became friends and a close relationship between our families soon developed. My mother and their mother, Eve, began chatting on the telephone two or three times a week. Brunches after church blossomed into dinners celebrating Christmas, New Year's Day, Easter, and Thanksgiving. Weekends at our cottage at Falcon Lake progressed to family holidays in the United States. The Buhrs were more than close friends; for almost thirty years, they were family.

Eve was diagnosed with terminal bowel cancer in April 1998, just six months after my own cancer recurred, and two months after my Uncle Peter had died of cancer of the oesophagus. My mother was devastated by her friend's illness. She visited the hospital nearly every day until Eve's death in June. In the following months, my mother avoided contact with Eve's husband, Bill, and with Janet, with whom my mother had been particularly close. She made up a variety of excuses for her reticence. *I was never really friends with Bill. Eve was my friend, not the rest of them.*

I knew that she found it too painful to have contact with the remaining Buhrs; when she saw the family it made her grieve Eve even more. Although I encouraged her to talk about her feelings, she was ardent in her refusal.

"Just let it go, Elizabeth," she said. "Eve is gone and that's the end of it."

My mother's relationship with the Buhrs soon ended and I'm ashamed to say that I didn't pursue our connection either. Still, I had been unable to hide my astonishment when three short years later my mother had failed to recognize our old friend.

"I'm sure you wouldn't have either," my mother replied imperiously. "She looks completely different. After all, I haven't seen her since she was ten years old."

I wasn't yet ready to publicly acknowledge my mother's disease by joining a support group, but I was starting to concede that her condition was beyond my control and that more difficult times were ahead. "I'm really supposed to refer clients to other resources," Daryl continued, "but since she won't see a doctor or accept any other assistance, I'll go check in on her from time to time."

AS WE EDGED towards Christmas 2005, the city was blanketed in white.

A late November storm had deposited several inches of snow, followed by smaller amounts in early December. After the first snowfall, I wasn't surprised to receive several panic-stricken telephone calls from my mother who had hired not one, but two people to shovel her driveway. Instead of firing one of them when she had first learned about her mistake, she allowed them both to arrive multiple times, one to shovel and one to discover that the work had already been done. My mother soon decided that I had hired the second snow removal person *behind her back*. She maintained that my motive was to prove that she *was going simple* or *had debenture*, or to further ensure that she would never again hold a valid driver's license. I felt her fresh anger with each snowfall and I began to dread the weather forecasts that predicted more precipitation was on the way.

"I might be going away for Christmas," my mother told me when I broached holiday plans in one of our more benign telephone conversations. "Anyway, I'm certainly not having Christmas with you after everything you've done."

The previous Christmas, my mother had wanted to spend time with us. Jeff chauffeured Davis, my mother and me to church on Christmas Eve, and then my mother spent the night at our house. The four of us had gone to Neil's house for brunch on Christmas Day and then we had enjoyed a quiet Christmas dinner together. My mother had opted to sleep at our house another night and stay until early evening on Boxing Day.

"Where would you go? " I asked, assuming that she was planning to visit Kevin, something she had always refused to consider because she thought she should be with Davis at Christmas. "Davis will be disappointed," I added, knowing that my words would make her feel guilty.

"Carol Winstanley is begging me to have Christmas with her in Ontario this year," my mother said.

Carol's last visit to our cottage had been so stressful that I doubted she wanted my mother to come for a Christmas visit.

"Why would you do that? Why wouldn't you spend Christmas with us, like always?"

I imagined my mother smiling in satisfaction at my distress.

"Because, Elizabeth, I don't want to."

Carol called me the next evening.

"Liz," Carol said. "I just want you to know it wasn't my idea for Mamie to come here for Christmas. She told me that she couldn't come to your house because you're mad at her."

"Not quite," I replied. "I want my mother with us over the holidays and I was hurt when she said she might be going to your place instead. So far she hasn't even told me it's a done deal. I figured it was all talk."

"Well, she's not coming now. She said that Davis was hysterical at the idea she wasn't going to be with you guys. But she did have a plane ticket. In fact, she had two. One on Air Canada and one on WestJet. She forgot she made the Air Canada reservation. I've made sure that everything is cancelled."

"Uh, okay, thanks."

I was stunned and didn't know what else to say.

I was beginning to feel as if we were engaged in a game of chess. My mother blocked every effort I made to restore our relationship while she calculated moves to push me further away. She was making up the rules; I was struggling to understand the objective of the game.

"Well, at least she told you what she was planning," Carol continued in a gentler voice. "She initially said she wasn't going to until she was at the airport, ready to leave." She paused. "You've got your hands full right now."

Shortly after my conversation with Carol, my mother called me and sweetly asked if I would take her to her local Safeway store. I dropped everything and drove to her house hoping she would still be in a welcoming mood when I arrived. I watched silently at the grocery store while my mother loaded her cart. When the cashier at the check-out stand asked her how she wanted to pay for her purchases my mother's blank stare implied that she was as unfamiliar with the necessities of everyday commerce as the Queen of England.

"Pay?" she asked blankly.

Before I could intervene she recovered and waved her Visa card uncertainly.

"Is this what you mean?" she asked.

On the drive home she told me that she had cancelled her trip to Ontario.

"So I guess I'll be coming to your place after all," she said.

"That's great, Mom," I assured her. "Will you spend the night on Christmas Eve as well?"

"I guess so," she replied.

On the morning of the twenty-fourth of December, I called my mother to confirm that I would pick her up at three o'clock.

"I'm having Christmas dinner with Mike and Muriel Zwarich," my mother told me curtly. "Not you."

"What?" I was apoplectic. "You said you were coming here."

"I'm going to the Zwarichs' and that's that," she told me.

I did my best to change my mother's mind but she wasn't having it. For the first time in a long time I hung up on my mother before she could hang up on me.

Every year since I was twelve years old, I had made a special effort to ensure that my mother had several packages under the tree. Even though I wouldn't be spending Christmas with my mother this year I still wanted her to have a few surprises to open that might make her remember the happy holidays we had shared.

I stopped by my mother's house on Boxing Day to deliver her gifts and to try to persuade her to come and watch Davis play hockey. She didn't answer when I rang the doorbell but out of the corner of my eye I saw the curtains in the living room part for a moment and then fall back into place. I rang the doorbell again and stepped back so I could see the front window more clearly. The curtains didn't move but I knew my mother knew I was there. I hung the white plastic bag full of presents on the handle of her front door and walked slowly back to my car.

Later, as I sat beside Jeff on the hard bench in the hockey arena, I couldn't bear the happy chatter of parents comparing their holiday celebrations.

"Hey, Liz, where's your Mom? We haven't seen her yet this year," someone asked.

The question made me shiver. I shrugged and concentrated on the figures gliding up and down the ice. Every movement reminded me of my mother's curtains closing as I stood on her front steps. I cheered when Jeff cheered and clapped when he clapped but I had no idea which team had scored or who had made the right play. The electric heater glowed red directly above me but I was filled with a cold dread that I couldn't shake.

My mother left a message on my answering machine a couple of days later. She said that she had received my presents, and while she was going to just throw them away, she couldn't resist opening them. Her saccharine voice became harsh and full of malice. She asserted that the presents were exactly the same as I had given her the year before and they were of no use to her. She said that I should *just get it through my head that she wanted nothing more to do with me because of all my dirty tricks.*

"Who are you and what have you done with my mother?" I shouted into the telephone. With my back against the wall, I slid to the floor, still holding the receiver.

Davis was watching me from the family room.

"Dad, come here. Something's wrong with Mom."

Jeff came running. Between sobs, I told him about my mother's message. He sat beside me on the floor and rubbed my back.

"Are you all right now?" he asked when I had finished crying.

I nodded. But he knew I wasn't.

I've never taken comfort from the wisdom of proverbs. My cynicism was reinforced by my experience: time did not heal all wounds and blood was not thicker than water. Yet against all odds, my hope sprang eternal and I clung to the belief that one day I would arrive at my mother's house and all would be forgiven and forgotten.

KALANSKY DIDN'T WRITE LETTER RE EARLY DEBENTURE.
LIZ WROTE LETTER & SIGNED KALANSKYS NAME. LIZ
LIKES TO REMIND ME I WILL NEVER DRIVE AGAIN –
SOMETHING I WILL NEVER DO IS HAVE ANYTHING TO
DO WITH HER AGAIN. I CONSIDER JEFF IS AS GUILTY
AS HER OR HE WOULD HAVE STOPPED HER IN HER
TRACKS LONG AGO. NEVER WILL I FORGET HER DIRTY
WAYS – BOTH TO BLAME – ALL WRITTEN OFF
GET LAWYER AND SETTLE THIS ONCE AND FOR ALL.

Re: told Chancel Guild people why I haven't been
to meetings for over a year.
They couldn't belive Liz would hold with that – so
said I think it was Liz not Kalansky that sent the
letter re: early debenture

Liz acknowledged she was the one that had my license taken away and for me never to get one again - will likely deny she ever told me this but its true

Elizabeth Murray married to Jeff Hirsch Some time ago at the cottage she was sitting by the front window and I took my cup of coffee and joined her there - she didn't seem talkative then she said I want you to sign the cottage over to me and never come down again. I went back to do my dishes in the sink. She went into the bedroom to tell Jeff, next thing they both come out and as they went through the front door stopped and said we will never be back. I stayed down for a few days, off and on she was ok. I think they bought soon after at Victoria Beach, built or bought another cottage at Victoria Beach. Now I assume they bought it so they could say they had it before any of this happened. Can tell she is gloating now that they pulled it off.

772-9988 Call to have will made out - first
also would like to talk over other
problem - Liz cottage & driving license
*appointment next Wed. morning
WAS TALKING TO FATHER HENRY
LAST WEEK AND WAS TELLING
HIM I NEEDED A GOOD LAWYER,
HE SUGGESTESTED YOU.
  I was talking to my daughter
last week, about getting
my drivers license back,
she said I would never
get it back. I haven't
had an accident in 69 yrs
I have been driving, only
one fine for speeding one
  Sunday morning for
  8:30 MASS - was going 60 in
  a 55 mile an hour zone -
  ($50.00 I think it was) hardly
another car on Pembina Hwy
was caught by one of the
signs on the posts.

LAWYER'S NAME
ADDRESS   PHONE NUMBER
WENT DOWN <u>LOST PAPER</u>
<u>HAD PUT NAME & ADDRESS ON PAPER IN MY POCKET</u>
<u>COULDN'T FIND IT — CALLED FATHER HENRY —</u>
<u>COULDN'T SPELL NAME EVEN</u>

WENT UP TO TOP FLOOR — STOOD
AROUND THERE FOR AWHILE — WENT DOWNSTAIRS
— CARETAKER CAME TALKING
TO ME — FELT SICK TO MY STOMACH — CAME HOME
LIZ HAD TOLD ME EVEN IF I
TRY DRIVERS TEST WILL
NEVER GET IT NOT EVEN IF
I MOVE TO ONTARIO

Henry I just felt that lawyer is against anyone over 80 is capable of driving - kept making references (sneakingly) re his fathers driving and old age. THINK I am far more active and capable, he may know Liz & Jeff a little better than he lets on - we never really discussed my driving re accidents or driving I don't feel over 80 and far more active than his father. Liz will even stop me from getting a license in Ontario - but have decided to sell up anyhow. Quite sure I sold the cottage last nite.

want to get my
drivers license back
spoke to a lawyer about it last
week - about making a will
and also this other nonsense - it takes
time to make a will out he brought
it over to the house to be verified yesterday
don't believe I signed it, but he ended up
saying I'll keep it in my safety deposit
box - I said I'll put it in mine, left word

LIZ CALLED TO SEE IF I WOULD GO TO DAVIS'S HOCKEY
MATCH - I REFUSED AND SAID AS I HAD
TOLD HER BEFORE I WOULDN'T GO
ANYMORE UNTIL I GOT MY DRIVERS LICENSE BACK -
AS SHE HAD TOLD ME I WOULD NEVER HAVE MY
LICENSE BACK -
HAVE FOUND OUT THE WHOLE THING IS CONTROLLED BY
LIZ. SHE HAS THE IDEA SHE CAN CONTROL MY LIFE -

# Chapter Thirteen

**"LIZ,"** **GOLDIE LOUCKS** said in her gravelly voice, "Just what's going on there? Something's not right with your mother. She's talking all sorts of nonsense about you."

I fought to compose myself. Goldie was one of my mother's closest and oldest friends in Campbellford. I hadn't spoken to any of my mother's acquaintances about her behaviour because I was afraid they might believe what she was saying about me. Goldie's denouncement of my mother's complaints made me feel as if someone had just tossed me a life preserver.

When I was finally able to talk, I told her what had been happening since the previous fall. Every once in a while she would mutter something like, "Oh, Liz," or, "I knew it".

The worst thing, I told her, was that she wouldn't see Davis. And he missed her so much.

"She told me you refused to let her see Davis," Goldie said indignantly. "I knew for sure that couldn't be true. And you know, Liz, in all these years, your mother has never said a bad thing about you. She's always been so proud of you. She's just not right in her head. My mother went that way too."

Goldie went on to tell me that she would pick up her mother from the nursing home every Sunday night for dinner and yet her mother would tell other people that her daughter *never bothered with her any more*.

"So I know what you're going through, Liz," she concluded. "Here's something you should think about, though. People used to tell me that my mother was taking it out on me because she loved me the most."

Since the beginning of January, my mother had only opened her door and allowed me into her front foyer on a few occasions. She would look at me with cold, dark eyes and tell me that she *wanted nothing more to do with me*, that I was *full of spite* and she *didn't know what she had done to make me so hateful*. She would sometimes tell me that *my father was right*; that he had always said that I was *nasty and mean* or some other derogatory descriptive that I know my father would never have said or thought, but that nevertheless hurt me to hear and made me question its validity if only for a second.

Most often, my mother wouldn't answer the door when I rang the bell or knocked. She would look out the front window and return to the kitchen. The diamond shaped panes of glass in the front door allowed me to watch her as she turned and walked away. Sometimes I would continue to watch as my mother repositioned herself at the kitchen table or her sewing machine with her head bent over a piece of fabric or a cup of tea and the newspaper. After a minute or so, she would look towards the door to see if I was still there. If she saw me she would shake her head, mouthing the words *go away* in what I imagined were capital letters.

No matter how often it happened, I was devastated as I stood outside peering into the house that had been my home for twenty-six years, knowing that my mother who was once my greatest advocate was purposely denying me entry.

As I drove up the street, my tears would soften the crisp lines of the houses and trees into a Monet watercolour, and I would press my cell phone against my ear to call Jeff and share my pain.

My mother was not solely at fault for our arguments. Sometimes, I would try to wound her, shatter her self-esteem; she would snap back with a litany of my weaknesses to reinforce how I disappointed her.

One day as I slowly approached the front step of my mother's house, I could see her sitting on the couch in the living room. She was bent over the coffee table, sorting through a haphazard pile of papers. When she looked up and saw me, I offered her a tentative smile and a little wave. She didn't return my gestures, but neither did she look away and pretend that she didn't see me. As I raised my hand to press the doorbell, I saw her move deliberately towards the foyer.

She swung open the door. "What do you want?" she asked. "You're not welcome after all of your dirty tricks."

She frowned and assumed a battle position: arms crossed over her chest, chin thrust forward ever so slightly.

My throat constricted. I recited the words I had said so many times before.

"Mom, I haven't done anything! I don't know what dirty tricks you're talking about."

"Oh yes, you do, Elizabeth. You and that Dr. Kalansky friend of yours. The two of you made sure my driver's license was taken away. You know you did."

"Okay, Mom, say I did have something to do with taking your license away, which I didn't. Can't you forgive me? Can't we move on?"

All that my mother heard was an admission of guilt.

"I'll never forgive you, Elizabeth. That's the last dirty trick you'll ever play on me."

She squared her shoulders, preparing for a brawl.

I recoiled as if she had slapped me with the palm of her hand.

"You call yourself a Christian. What about forgiveness? What kind of Christian are you if you can't forgive?" I said.

"Now you want to take my church away from me too?" My mother's cheeks were turning red. "I suppose you're going to phone Father Henry and tell him how terrible I am."

"Mom, that's not what I'm saying. I'm just trying –"

"You're just trying to ruin my life, that's what you're trying." Her eyes welled. "That's fine, Elizabeth. I won't go to church any more. I'll give you what you want."

I pictured a mother and daughter holding hands on the steps of Holy Trinity Anglican Church on an Easter Sunday. I was a chubby six year old wearing a lilac coat and she was an elegant woman in pale pink. I wanted us to be like that again, without the anger and resentment that was now dividing us. I was surprised by the strength of my longing.

I watched a tear seep from my mother's eye. She maintained her defiant stance but she no longer looked like she wanted to fight; she looked tired and confused. I was ashamed of myself. With my arms outstretched, I took a step towards my mother. She shook her head and took a step back.

"Oh, no you don't. Just go. Just go and leave me alone." The tear was now midway down my mother's cheek. "For once in your life, Elizabeth, JUST LEAVE ME ALONE."

JUST AS I had almost reconciled myself to the fact that my relationship with my mother was never going to improve, I made a major breakthrough. One afternoon at the end of May as I turned the corner to her house, I noticed an unfamiliar red sedan in the driveway.

My mother had left the front door open to allow a breeze to flow through the screened panel in the storm door. I paused and tried to listen to the voices I could hear in the living room. From years of experience, I knew how to jiggle the handle on the storm door to release the catch even if the lock was engaged but I decided it would be better to ring the doorbell.

"What are you doing here?"

My mother looked through the screen with narrowed eyes. The voices were silent now so I assumed my mother had only one visitor.

"I just stopped by to see how you're doing," I said.

"That's none of your business. It's not like you really care anyway, Elizabeth."

She turned her head towards the living room. Her expression became slightly less hostile as she reached out and unlocked the door.

"Well, since you're here, you might as well come in."

I slowly followed my mother into the house. At first glance everything seemed to be in order. There were two large, untidy piles of magazines and other papers on the coffee table but the shelves displaying my mother's collection of Royal Doulton and other figurines seemed to be dust free; the visible part of the kitchen counter was only moderately cluttered with more papers and a jar of strawberry jam.

My mother sat in a chair hugging her chest with her arms, one leg crossed over the other. A tall man with glasses perched on the edge of the couch, kitty corner from the chair my mother had chosen.

"This is Dr. Dyck, the man who comes to read my head." My mother looked first at Daryl and then at me with a sardonic half-smile. "He's trying to prove that I'm crazy."

Although I had spoken to Daryl on the telephone many times, we had never met. He stood and we shook hands as I introduced myself. Our eyes reached a silent agreement that we wouldn't reveal our previous communication.

"Daryl Dyck. I'm a geriatric clinician, not a doctor."

Daryl returned to his position on the couch. I sat on a chair across from him. My mother remained sitting, swinging her foot impatiently.

"I was telling your mother that I wanted to go through a quick cognition test with her – just to check her memory and see how she's doing."

He was watching my mother as he spoke, obviously trying to gauge her reaction to his suggestion.

"I told Dr. Dyck my memory is fine for a woman my age." My mother glared at me and then offered Daryl a flirtatious smile. "But if he wants me to take a test, I'll take a test."

I tried not to move a muscle.

"Okay, then, that's great," Daryl said. "It won't take long. I'm going to say three words, and get you to repeat them. I want you to remember the words, and in a few minutes I'm going to ask you what they are. Is that okay with you?"

My mother nodded and Daryl continued.

"Okay, the three words are cat, ball, and house. Cat. Ball. House. Can you repeat them for me, please?"

"Cat, ball, house."

My mother smirked.

"That's right. Cat, ball, house," Daryl repeated. "Now I want you to remember those words and in a little while I'll get you to tell me what they are. Okay?"

My mother nodded again. She clearly thought this test was not going to be too difficult.

"Can you tell me what year it is?" Daryl asked.

She looked at him with disgust.

"2006," she answered correctly.

My mother also correctly answered that the current month was May but didn't do as well with the day of the week. Her guess was Wednesday when it was actually Thursday but as she said, when you don't work, it's easy to lose track of the days.

Daryl handed my mother a piece of paper and a pen.

"Now, I'd like you to draw a clock for me."

She looked confused.

"The shape of the clock's face and the numbers, just like a clock you'd see on a wall," he clarified.

I looked at the antique clock sitting on the mantle, an heirloom from my paternal grandfather. The timepiece was green marble with gold columns and made me think of a stately southern manor. My gaze wandered to the collection of photographs on the end of the mantle farthest from the clock. Something was different. My law school graduation picture, which had been proudly displayed since 1985, was missing. Also banished were the photos from my wedding day – one of Jeff and me together and one of me alone. The simple gold-edged frame we had given my parents the first Christmas we were married was now filled with pictures of Neil and Barb's children. There were several pictures of Kevin and his family as well as Megan and Graeme's current school photos. The absence of any images of me was a stinging metaphor of my disappearance from her life.

My mother finished her drawing and held it up for Daryl's inspection. The face of the clock was roughly circular, but the numbers were awkwardly spaced. The number one was in its proper position but the twelve was at the eight o'clock position with all of the other numbers crowded in between. The inaccuracies shocked me.

"That's fine."

Daryl smiled gently at my mother. She sat back in her chair, pleased with her performance.

"Now, I told you three words a few minutes ago and asked you to remember them. Can you tell me what those words are?"

My mother paused for a moment. She was less smug than she had been earlier. "Oh, I don't know. Was one of the words dog?" Her top leg was swinging vigorously. She shrugged. "You've been talking too much for me to remember words you said at the beginning of our conversation. I bet you can't remember words I said, either."

In spite of her bravado, my mother looked worried. I wanted to lean over and whisper the answer in her ear. Daryl laughed and my mother's shoulders relaxed.

"Sometimes it's hard to remember everything," he said. Daryl left a short time later. My mother walked him to the door.

"It was good to meet your daughter," I heard Daryl say.

She mumbled something in response.

"No, you're lucky to have her," Daryl said firmly.


My mother was hemming a pair of pants when I arrived the following afternoon. She answered the door but returned to her task with a remarkable fixity of purpose.

"All of my slacks are too long," she told me. "I guess I've shrunk."

There were three more pairs of pants in various stages of repair on the table beside her sewing machine. The pants she was wearing stopped at the middle of her ankle.

"I don't know, Mom. Maybe be careful you're not shortening then too much."

"I know how to shorten slacks, Elizabeth. I don't like them dragging on the ground."

She conceded to let me drive her to Super Clips where she insisted on having so much of her hair shorn that she looked like she was recovering from chemotherapy. I didn't say a word. We returned to the grocery store to finish shopping for items she had missed the day before. When she supplemented yesterday's donut purchase with a second dozen, I didn't protest.

On the drive home when she maintained yet again that she was not going to see Davis until she had her driver's license back, I had to break my silence. My mother hadn't had any contact with our son since the previous Thanksgiving but still she refused to come and see him or allow me to bring him to see her. I knew Davis was missing his grandmother, and I knew my mother would be missing Davis even more.

"You know, Mom, you think you're punishing me by staying away but you're really punishing yourself and Davis. You're cutting off your nose to spite your face," I said, parroting one of the expressions she had frequently recited when I was young.

She shook her head but didn't respond.


THE PHONE RANG just before eight o'clock that evening.

"Liz", my mother said, her voice wavering, "I'd like to see Davis. Would you please bring him over?"

"Now?" I asked.

"Why not? Won't he want to come?"

She was expressing her greatest fear.

"Of course he'll want to come," I said, although I wasn't really sure how Davis would react. "We'll be right there."

Davis didn't hesitate for a second. All winter he had blamed me for my mother's absence. "Why did you have to argue with her?" he asked, referring to her abrupt departure from our Thanksgiving dinner. Now, he didn't care why, when, or how. He just wanted to see his grandmother. Jeff was more cautious.

"Maybe I should come too," he offered, "just in case."

My mother met us at the door with her arms outstretched for her grandson. At not quite thirteen, he hadn't yet started the transformation from boy to man but even so my once strong mother looked as delicate as a willow branch in his arms. As he returned my mother's hug and they squeezed each other for an extra few seconds, I could see her face swell with joy, relief and love. Davis gently patted my mother's back, instinctively bestowing the comfort that she silently craved. Jeff and I were both holding back tears.

We didn't stay long. Davis had homework to finish and I was exhausted from the emotion of the day. As we were driving home, Jeff and I agreed that maybe, just maybe, we had turned some sort of corner.

As I opened the door from the garage I could hear the telephone ringing. With a sinking feeling I saw it was my mother.

"Oh, Liz? Would you mind coming back here? Just you. I want to talk something over with you."

It was now a few minutes after ten o'clock. I wasn't prepared for a third visit in one day but she did call me Liz rather than Elizabeth so I knew I should take advantage of her conciliatory attitude.

"Um, okay, Mom."

"Just you," my mother repeated.

My mother met me at the door for the second time that evening. Her arms were not outstretched.

"Come on in. I thought we should talk and clear the air."

I followed my mother into the kitchen. She sat in her usual spot at the end of the table and picked up a few pieces of paper that had been waiting on her placemat. I sat at the table immediately to her right.

"Okay, Mom. What's up? What do you want to talk about?"

"I want to clear the air," she said again. "I want to know why you were in cahoots with that Dr. Kalansky to take away my driver's license."

"Mom, we've been through this again and again. I had nothing to do with you losing your driver's license. Nothing."

I struggled to keep my voice even.

"Elizabeth, I know you did. I have proof. It says so right here."

"There can't be proof of something I didn't do." I reached for the papers. "Can I see?"

My mother clutched the papers in her fist and moved them farther away from me. She considered her position.

"I guess so. But just quickly. I need them."

She handed me her odd collection of lined paper and old envelopes. A thin piece of notepaper slipped out in the transfer. The name of a real estate company and an agent was printed at the top of the page. I could see LIZ SPITEFUL LICENSE printed in dark pencil strokes in my mother's handwriting. I flipped through the papers in my hand. *Took away my license because I wouldn't give her Falcon Lake cottage* said one. *Liz friends with Dr. Kalansky,* began another. A couple of the notes were long and went into detail about all of my wrongdoings.

"Mom, these don't prove anything. They're just a bunch of your own notes with stuff you've made up. "

I tossed the papers back onto the table in front of my mother.

My mother scratched her head. Her forehead furrowed as she looked at one of the papers and then another.

"It says right here what you did. It says you took my –"

"Mom", I interrupted. "Those are just *your* words. They aren't facts. And they're not true." I shook my head at her. "They. Are. Not. True."

My mother continued to shuffle through her papers.

"Mom, if you want to clear the air, you've got to accept that I didn't take your driver's license away. Can't you do that? "

She lifted her head and looked in my direction but her eyes didn't meet mine. She bit her lip.

"I'm not sure. I just don't know what to believe anymore. "

I stood up.

"Then there's nothing more I can say. I'm going home now. "

*How did we get into this mess?* I wondered. I was almost in the front hallway when my mother called me.

"Liz, come back. Please."

Part of me wished I had walked a little faster but I returned to the kitchen and sat down at the table. After five seconds I broke the silence.

"What's it going to be, Mom?"

"I just wish you hadn't gotten in with that Dr. Kalansky."

"No!"

I hit the table with my open palm. My mother flinched. I softened my tone.

"No, Mom. I'm not going to keep talking about this. You've got to get over it."

She looked down at her papers again, one elbow on the table, her hand supporting her head.

"I just don't know," she muttered, more to herself than to me.

I stood up again.

"I'm going home now, Mom. I can't keep telling you the same thing over and over."

I made it to my car this time. With the driver's door open, I saw my mother standing on the front step.

"Don't go," she called.

A memory of a long-ago fight with my mother flooded over me. I was nine or ten and for some reason I didn't want to go back to school after lunch. I left the house sobbing and got halfway across the front lawn before I returned to the house to yell something petulant like *you don't even care!*

I repeated the sequence a couple of times, leaving and returning, crying loudly to make sure that my mother understood my despair, until she finally gave in and allowed me to stay home. I had been in control of that situation. This time I had no idea how to persuade my mother to see things my way.

I closed the car door and followed my mother inside. We stood in the front hallway. I put my arms around her.

"I love you, Mom."

"I love you too, Liz." She pushed back and wiped her eyes with the tissue she pulled out of one sleeve of her cardigan.

"I know, Mom. I know."

And I did know, although it had been so many difficult months since I had heard her say it that I sometimes forgot.

We hadn't really resolved anything but for the next few weeks my relationship with my mother settled into a new normal. While our telephone communication wasn't any better, she no longer refused me entry into the house. Sometimes she allowed me to drive her to the grocery store or the drugstore or the bank; sometimes she maintained that she *didn't want any help from me*. On one occasion, I drove her to the bank but she refused to let me drive her home. While she stood at the bus stop, I sat in my car watching to make sure she got on the right bus and hoped that she would change her mind.

I was constantly measuring how wide my mother opened the door, how many centimetres her mouth turned down when she saw me, how long she looked at me without hatred in her eyes. I filed away the numbers, hoping that a later analysis would reveal the secret to maintaining our tentative peace.

Surviving cancer had altered my priorities; time became precious and I was compelled to make as many positive memories for my son as I could. I wanted Davis to treasure our little rituals like shaping his favourite sugar cookie dough into dinosaurs, cuddling in an oversized armchair in front of the fireplace or riding our bikes to the playground on warm spring evenings. I wanted him to remember Christmases and birthdays and summers at the cottage, but what I really wanted was for him to remember me: my smell; my touch; the sound of my voice telling him how much I loved him. I was afraid that I all I would remember about my mother after she was gone was her hatred. I was afraid that her behaviour now was destroying all of my memories of the good times we had shared.

Kevin -

was the reason you started DR DICK coming to the
house to see if I was normal or not. When he was
here the last time Liz just showed up and just
sat there and listened to everything. Actually I
believe all this started when Kalansky wrote that
letter re debenture, don't think it was Kalansky that
wrote it, I believe Liz did and signed her name.
Liz called Goldie in Campbellford saying how mean
I had been never going over to see Davis or to go
to any of his hockey games etc. Goldie called and
bawled me out. I never mentioned to Liz that I
knew she had phoned Goldie in Campbellford but
one day she came out with how Goldie had called
her. She's trying to break my friendships up down
there - must call Marion Fleming to-nite to see if Liz
called her.

Liz says why live in the past, shouldn't
we forget the past and live for the
future, thinks we should be compatible
but THEN SHE COMPLAINED that sometimes
I don't answer my door when she comes to
the house. THERE'S A GOOD REASON FOR IT.
She always wanted her own way. When her
father was living he used to get fed up
with her.
Never trust Liz again no matter what.
(That paper was not written by Kalansky
but by Liz)
Notice Liz never brings Davis over so much
- must forget about him, all but memories
of him laying in front of fireplace with
John and every time John got up he would
open his eyes and watch where he went
- Liz will make sure I never see Davis
again so I've made up my mind to forget
him

Just waking up as to what Liz has been up to the past 3 or 4 years - this whole driver license thing was all her doing, because I wouldn't give her the cottage she told me she would see to it that I couldn't drive any more

WHEN I WENT TO KALANSKYS FOR A CHECK UP some years ago - I waited around for awhile, then decided to come home, was going somewhere for dinner that nite, anyhow next morning around 10 AM she phoned me, absolutely livid, told me I shouldn't have come home without her permission, very angrily she said you be down at my office by 3:30

never heard anything until I was writing Xmas cards when this letter came supposedly from Kalansky saying I could no longer drive a car as I had early debenture

then a man came to the door, he said he was from drivers licensing and I had to give him my drivers license,

after that I called the Police Department and a ~~policeman~~ Mounted Policeman came out - I told him the whole story and he said he had checked the department and it was a complaint that had gone in. He wouldn't give me any details - he talked me into joining the Mounted Policemans club in Toronto - next thing I know I had a letter from Toronto asking for a donation to Policemans something or other - I

still get a notice but this year I didn't send
anything.

I think it was after the first snow fall that
year when I called Liz to ask her something
and she answered right away if you think your
getting your drivers license back your not - I
just let the remark slide, and said I had got
someone to shovel the laneway out. (think the
first snow fall was heavy that year)

First part of September Liz brought me a
pair of Davis school pants to be shortened.
~~Anyhow I went over for Xmas dinner~~ Shortly
after there was an occasion when I went over
for dinner - think the food was just slopped on
the table - after dinner Jeff got up and went into
the living room, I helped clean the table off,
they had painted one of the long doors near the
sink a shiny black color. I remarked on it and
she said can't you remember anything its always
been like that,

then started asking me if I didn't remember
having pneumonia at her place, and how Dr.
Kalansky came over and checked on me - I
remembered the illness part but not who the
doctor was - didn't want to talk about Kalansky
so asked her to drive me home - haven't talked to
her much since

Anyhow I think she has been trying to get back
at me ever since, Its odd, you know, Liz can

be so nice yet underneath must have a lot of hatred for me, and I think the start of it was when I wouldn't let her have the ruddy cottage. They bought their own cottage shortly after that but that was just for show

She, I believe, was the instigator of this debenture bit with Kalansky to get even

FEELING DOWN IN THE DUMPS LATELY —
LIZ SEEMS TO HAVE HAD SO MUCH SPITE — FIRST IT
WAS THROUGH HER WANTING THE COTTAGE TURNED OVER
TO HER — AND ME NEVER TO GO DOWN AGAIN.
EVER SINCE SEEMS SHE HAS TRIED ALL KINDS OF
MEANNESS
IT WAS HER THAT HAD MY LICENSE TAKEN AWAY —
GUESS I WASN'T THINKING RE HER JEALOUSY

DREAM
WOKE UP PEOPLE STANDING
OVER ME — SAYING SHE CAN'T
DRIVE ANY MORE — TOO DANGEROUS

# Chapter Fourteen

AT THE END of June 2006, Davis and I were getting ready to move to Victoria Beach for the summer. In other years, I had relied on Jeff to bring supplies on weekends and had only come into the city once or twice between the end of June and the beginning of September. My plan was to check on my mother once a week, with Jeff supplementing my visit with a weekly visit of his own. I had learned from a friend of a friend that Kevin had bought a cottage in Manitoba and I wondered if my mother would join the family for a portion of their visit. I emailed him to ask him to keep me apprised of his plans.

Kevin replied that my mother wanted to see a lawyer and get me out of her life once and for all. His words hurt. I was offended that he seemed to accept my mother's complaints against me and I wanted to scold him for not supporting me.

MY MOTHER WAS not unhappy to see me when I managed to connect with her over the summer but our contact was sporadic. My brother's lack of communication and my mother's habitual refusal to answer the telephone made it difficult to know if she was at her house in the city or with Kevin. I finally resorted to asking her neighbour, Muriel Zwarich, to call me when my mother was at home so Jeff or I could go and see her.

On one visit at the end of August, my mother told me over a cup of tea that Muriel's daughter, Gail, had driven her to a Driver and Vehicle Licensing office a couple of weeks earlier. According to my mother, she was told she could have her driver's license back if she passed a simple driving test. I knew that her report couldn't be true.

"You received a letter that set out the process you had to follow to have your license reinstated," I reminded her. "It said you had to take a written test, and if you passed that, you had to have a road test with an occupational therapist."

I left out the part about having a medical form completed by her family physician. My mother set her mug of tea down so firmly a little liquid sloshed onto the table.

"I know what I heard, Elizabeth. I could have had my driving test right then and there, except it was late and they were closing down for the day." Her eyes narrowed. "Gail's been busy, or she would've taken me back for my test last week."

My mother was dabbing at her spilled tea with a tissue she produced from the sleeve of her sweater. Her neck and shoulders were rigid. I pushed back my chair, retrieved a dishcloth from the sink, and handed it to her. She took the cloth but didn't acknowledge my silent offer of contrition.

"If you want, I'll take you to the driver licensing place tomorrow afternoon," I suggested. "Just don't get your hopes up."

The next day, I arrived at one o'clock, the hour we had agreed upon the day before. I reached out to open the door but the handle wouldn't turn.

I could hear the faint whistle of the kettle starting to boil – not the strident screech of water left too long, but the gradual increase in intensity when the pressure is just starting to mount. I fumbled for the key I kept at the bottom of my purse. When I was leaving the house a few months earlier, I had noticed two shiny, silver keys lying on the marble-topped console in the entry along with an invoice from Noble Locksmith. A third key was already in the deadbolt in the front door. I slid one of the keys into my pocket for safekeeping.

The pilfered key turned the lock and the door yielded.

"Mom?" I called as I stepped into the front entry.

No answer. I walked into the kitchen and unplugged the now screaming kettle.

"Mom?" I called again.

My mother came up the stairs from the family room with a basket of laundry in her arms. Her hair formed a wispy halo around her head; the blue and yellow flannel shirt she had tucked into elastic waist pants looked too heavy for the unseasonably warm day.

"How did you get in?" she demanded.

"What do you mean? The door was open and I walked in," I lied.

"I was sure the door was locked!" My mother looked at me suspiciously. "What are you doing here, anyway?"

"I thought we were going to see about your driver's license," I said. "I told you yesterday we could go this afternoon." I stopped myself just before I added *don't you remember?*

"That's not what you told me at all."

The ironing board, which now seemed to be a permanent fixture in the middle of the kitchen, shook with the force of the laundry basket landing on it soundly. She scowled.

"You told me you were going to see to it that I would never get my driver's license back."

I wanted to throw up my hands and tell my mother that she was right but I managed a more conciliatory approach.

"Why am I here, then? Come on, Mom, get ready and let's go."

My mother stared at me for a second before she retreated to the family room and disappeared into the adjacent bathroom.

"Okay, then," my mother said when she reappeared a few minutes later. She had brushed her hair and applied a pale lipstick that extended slightly above the top of her lip line. Her attempt was passable so I didn't suggest that she remove the lipstick and try again. She retrieved her purse from a chair in the dining room and produced a set of keys.

"We have to take my car. I'm going to need it for the driving test."

I had assumed that her car hadn't been driven in the two years since she had lost her license.

"Is it insured?" I asked.

My mother looked at me blankly.

"I don't know what you mean by insured," she said. "But I've paid all of the bills I get for the car. I want it ready for when I get my license back."

My mother couldn't confirm that one of the bills she had paid was for car insurance, and couldn't see why it was an issue in any event. She told me that Gail Zwarich drove her car *all the time without worrying about whether or not it was insured.* I blanched at the thought that my mother was keeping her car operational but decided to leave that battle for another day. I ran to check the glove compartment of the car where her current insurance papers were neatly filed in a plastic sleeve.

The address we were looking for was in the middle of a small suburban strip mall, sandwiched between a florist shop and a hair salon. A sign on the door identified the office as "Manitoba Public Insurance – Driver Licensing."

A long counter separated a waiting area at the front from the open work stations and glass fronted offices at the back. A woman behind the counter was studying a computer screen and speaking to a young man wearing brown corduroy pants and a jean jacket. There was no one else waiting in line. I sat in a grey metal chair in the row farthest from the counter.

"I'm going to sit right here, Mom, while you talk to the lady. I'm not coming with you because if you don't get what you want, I don't want you to blame me."

My mother sat on the chair beside me with her purse in her lap. One of her hands was twisting the purse's leather strap while the other gripped the front of her chair so tightly that her knuckles were turning white. She was moving her lips but no sound was coming out.

The man in the corduroy pants was now sitting in the front row, fidgeting in his chair. The woman had returned to one of the desks behind the counter and was typing furiously. I nudged my mother.

"Come on, there's no one in line. You can go right up."

She started walking slowly towards the counter, holding her purse in front of her like a brown leather shield, a weary knight ready to do battle for the last time. The woman at the counter didn't look up from her typing. A second woman in her mid-thirties came forward wearing a broad smile. She adjusted her blouse to ensure that the button between her breasts was providing sufficient coverage, and tucked her dark hair behind one ear.

"What can I do for you today?" she asked my mother.

"I'm here to get my driver's license back," my mother answered in a surprisingly confident voice.

I couldn't hear the next exchange but the woman began entering information into the computer on the counter. Her smile dimmed slightly as she stopped typing and began reading the screen in front of her. My mother leaned forward and craned her neck in an effort to see what had captured the woman's interest.

"It looks like your license has been suspended for medical reasons," the woman said too loudly, as if she suddenly wasn't sure if my mother understood English.

"There's nothing wrong with me," my mother insisted just as loudly. "That doctor wrote that I have debenture out of spite."

The woman looked sceptical.

"That may be," she said gently. "But when your license has been suspended for medical reasons, there's a process you have to follow to get it back. You must have received a letter setting all of that out."

"I didn't get any letter," my mother said. "I'm telling you, that doctor was just acting out of spite. There's no reason I can't drive my car. I haven't even had an accident."

The man in the corduroy pants sniggered. I cleared my throat loudly to get his attention and gave him a disdainful glare when he glanced back at the noise.

The woman was still talking to my mother but I could no longer hear what they were saying. She patted my mother's hand and walked to the back of the room to collect a corpulent male colleague. The pair glided over to the counter like a tugboat guiding an ocean liner to port. The woman pointed at the computer screen and spoke while the man nodded. His substantial frame towered over my mother.

"I'm sorry, Ma'am," he said, "but we can't give you your driver's license back today."

My mother looked disbelieving.

"But the doctor was just being spiteful," she repeated.

The man reiterated that there was a process my mother had to follow and that she ought to have received a letter that set out everything she had to do. My mother shook her head in response. Finally the man told my mother he would send her a copy of the letter that had accompanied her notice of suspension. If she wanted her driver's license back, she should follow its instructions.

My mother turned to look at me. Confusion spread over her face. She had no idea what had just happened.

When the telephone rang later that evening I knew it had to be my mother.

"You just had to do it, didn't you, Elizabeth?"

"Do what?" I asked in complete bewilderment.

"Don't play innocent with me," my mother replied. "You held up that sign that said debenture."

"I did what?" I asked again.

The phone went dead. I sat with the receiver against my ear, listening to the static emptiness.

MY MOTHER'S DETERMINATION to blame me for the loss of her license had created new ways to measure the passage of time. How many Easters, Thanksgivings and Labour Day weekends had she spent without me? How many birthdays and family celebrations had she chosen to miss? Milestones such as Davis' birth or my father's death didn't warrant the same kind of attention now. Now it was all about life before and after the date my mother lost her freedom to drive.

December 2006 marked the second Christmas I spent without my mother. Carol Winstanley told me that my mother had accepted an invitation to Neil's house for a Christmas lunch and it hurt that she would attend the holiday celebration without me.

Neil and Barb had moved into a new house in the spring of 2002. They arranged a family dinner to show off their new home that July, when Kevin and his family were in town. When my mother learned that I hadn't been invited because Kevin was to attend, she insisted that Barb correct the oversight.

"I'm not going to a family dinner without you and Jeff and Davis," my mother told me.

When Carol phoned on the morning of December twenty-eighth, I assumed that she was phoning to provide me with additional details about how my mother had spent the holiday. We exchanged pleasantries but as soon as I heard her voice I could sense that something was wrong.

"Is your doll collection still at Mamie's?" she asked.

I confirmed that it was.

"Well, you might want to bring it to your place," Carol said. "Mamie told me that she was going to give all your dolls to the church. I know some of them might be valuable –" Her voice trailed off.

My mother had encouraged me to start collecting dolls when I was seven or eight years old. She saved countless labels from aerosol cans of Reddi-wip whipped topping and mailed them away for a dozen or so nine-inch plastic dolls, each wearing the national dress of a different country. My mother then enlisted her friends and acquaintances to *pick up a doll for Liz* whenever they travelled outside of Canada and my collection grew to include souvenirs from around the world.

When my mother had been a young girl in the late 1920s, she had longed for an Eaton Beauty doll. The lifelike dolls with unglazed china heads, fully jointed bodies, sleep eyes and mohair wigs were advertised every year in the T. Eaton Co.'s fall and winter catalogue. The Beauties cost less than two dollars each but forty years later I could still hear my mother's regret as she explained that her parents could never afford to buy her one.

I found my first doll with a china head in the window of The Old Curiosity Shoppe in downtown Winnipeg when I was ten years old. Its glazed face had painted eyes and hair and its china arms and legs were attached to a cloth body. The clerk told me that the doll was a reproduction of a popular German model from the late 1800s. It didn't matter to me that the doll wasn't an Eaton Beauty or even an antique. I thought she was beautiful.

For several months I visited the antique shop every time I was downtown. One Saturday, the doll's little wooden chair was empty. My mother bit her lip to hide her smile when I told her my disappointing news. I had put the doll at the top of my Christmas wish list even though the price tag of thirty-five dollars had seemed impossibly extravagant. When I found the doll under the tree on Christmas morning, my mother's smile was as wide as mine.

After that, my mother and I decided to include antique dolls in my collection. One was purchased from a collectibles store in South Dakota when we stopped during a family road trip to Wisconsin. Two more came from a classified ad that my mother placed in a paper in Warrington, England when she and Kevin and I visited her cousins in 1976. My prize – a bisque-headed doll with a leather body and real human hair manufactured in the late 1890s – was purchased in Bath when my mother and father and I returned to England in 1979. We searched but we never managed to find an Eaton Beauty.

I thanked Carol for the call and moved to an oversized armchair in our family room. The fingers on my right hand tapped the notes of a piano sonata on my thigh. Although I hadn't played the piano in a serious way since I was in university, twelve years of lessons had left an indelible mark in my memory and I often played soundless melodies when I was confused, upset or lost in thought. At that moment, I was livid that my mother was going to give away my dolls and heartbroken that she would even consider doing so.

My mother's living room curtains were open and she was standing in front of the window with her arms crossed as I walked up her front steps. The door opened. Stay calm; be reasonable, I repeated silently as I stepped into the foyer. Her now familiar greeting was disdainful.

"What do you want, Elizabeth?" she said.

My mother hadn't allowed me in her house for at least two weeks. The absence of a tree and other Christmas decorations surprised me. This was the first year that my mother hadn't erected the artificial Christmas tree we had bought together the year Davis was two years old, or hung tiny coloured lights around the mirror above the fireplace. When I was young, my mother had decorated the house from top to bottom. A plastic Santa in his sleigh with all eight reindeer flew up the staircase; a four-foot tall snowman guarded our gifts and stockings, and our everyday coffee mugs and glasses were replaced with their candy cane counterparts.

I stepped around my mother and walked to the corner of the room where my doll cabinet still stood. My mother was close behind me. The antique case that had once belonged to my Grandfather Murray was almost empty of its former precious contents. Behind the glass doors, I could see a jumble of ceramic knick-knacks, old teacups and saucers and an assortment of books and papers. A ragged souvenir doll from Mexico was propped next to a tired looking Barbie and three of my Reddi-wip dolls. All of my antique dolls were missing. I turned to my mother.

"Mom, where are my dolls?"

"What dolls?" My mother was looking somewhere over my shoulder to avoid making eye contact. Her mouth was curved into a smirk. She pretended to think for a moment.

"Oh yes. I gave some of your dolls to Father Henry for the nursery at the church. And I gave some more to Sara the other day, when she brought me back from lunch at Neil's. She said she could use them in her classroom."

"You gave my china-headed dolls to Father Henry and Sara?"

My chin dropped and my cheeks started to burn.

My mother's smirk-smile dropped away. Her eyes became cloudy but her posture remained defiant.

"I don't think any of them had china heads."

I turned my back on my mother and began making a more detailed inventory of my loss. I didn't want to listen to what she had to say.

"They're not toys, you know," I told her testily. "They're not for kids to play with."

I glanced over my shoulder to gauge her reaction. I saw an old woman who looked oddly afraid, even with her arms folded across her chest and her jaw jutting forward. My ballooning frustration deflated as if it had been stabbed with a pin. I couldn't fight with my mother now. The power imbalance was too great. I opened the door of the cabinet and began removing dolls, placing them carefully on floor beside me.

"What are you doing? Those are mine!" she scolded.

I ignored her and continued to sort through the debris in the cabinet, plucking out a porcelain baby doll whose head swivelled to show a laughing face on one side and a crying face on the other. I had used my babysitting earnings to purchase her when I was in Grade Nine and she had always been one of my favourites.

"You can't have that one," my mother said loudly. "I bought that one after you left home."

I stood up and took a step towards the kitchen to find a bag so I could carry my diminished collection home. My mother shuffled to the right to block my path. The smirk-smile was back on her face and her gaze didn't falter.

"Maybe I should call the police and tell them what you're doing."

"Go right ahead, Mom."

I decided to forgo a bag and sat back down.

"No, I know what I'm going to do. I'm going to call the *Free Press* and tell them that you took away my driver's license, and now you're stealing my dolls too."

She rocked back and forth on her heels, delighted with her idea.

I didn't take her bait. I scooped up my dolls and cradled them in both arms as I quickly walked towards the foyer. Unwilling to surrender my cargo for a second, I slipped my feet into my boots and fumbled with the door.

In the safety of my car, I squeezed my eyes shut and willed my heart to stop racing. I should have reclaimed my doll collection years ago but it didn't fit with our contemporary décor and, in any event, I had wanted to avoid another piano incident.

As soon as Jeff and I had moved into our first house two years after we were married, my mother began agitating for me to take my piano. *I don't want it in my living room anymore. It takes up too much space.* If you don't want it, I'm going to give it away. After listening to my mother's complaints for a year, I called a moving company and made the arrangements to have the piano transported from my mother's house to mine. My mother changed her mind as I told her the plan.

"I like to look at the piano and remember how you used to sit and practice," she said.

I cancelled the moving company and left the piano in my mother's living room for another two years.

A few days after I had reclaimed my dolls from my mother's china cabinet, I stopped at Neil and Barb's house to retrieve the dolls that had been given to Sara. None of them were my cherished antiques.

"Mom keeps calling for us to come over so we've been trying to go more often." Barb's voice drifted away. "Do you know that Mom is really mad at you?" she asked.

I nodded.

"It's a little hard to miss."

Over the years, my relationship with Neil and Barb had turned from amicable to reserved. After Sara and Mathew were born, Barb was understandably hurt by my mother's lack of interest in her grandchildren and her determination to isolate them from my father. She began sharing her complaints about my mother with increasing frequency. I often agreed with

Barb's position but that didn't mean I was prepared to accept her criticisms. If lines had to be drawn, there was no question of my loyalties, regardless of who I thought had the worthier position. My mother was my mother; Barb was just my sister-in-law. I found it more and more difficult to maintain a relationship with Neil and Barb and with some regret I chose to distance myself from them. It was simply the easiest thing to do.

Neil and Kevin hadn't always been close but as my relationship with Kevin had deteriorated, his ties to Neil had strengthened. It wasn't long before the two had formed a strong alliance that made my tentative connection with Neil even more difficult to sustain.

Neil laughed and said that my mother had told them about the sign I had held up at the driver's licensing office. He added that when my mother had come to their house for Christmas lunch the other guests wondered why she had used red lipstick to line her eyebrows.

"I'm really concerned about how long Mom can stay in the house," I replied. "I'm not sure it's safe for her anymore."

Neil and Barb both nodded.

"You know Kevin has never said a bad word about you to me," Neil said, changing the subject abruptly.

"That's great," I replied. "I haven't said anything negative to you about Kevin, either."

Neil paused. "No, I guess you haven't," he agreed.

The detente my mother had declared at the beginning of the summer had been slowly dissolving and was now officially over. The tenuous renewal of our relationship made the resumption of hostilities even more distressing. My mother's belief that I had done unforgivable things caused me immeasurable pain and I was demoralized that her failing memory had also made her forget her love for me. I was left feeling lost and somehow disjointed, worried that I wouldn't have my brothers' support as I continued the battle against my mother's dementia.

42 Thatcher Drive
Winnipeg, Mb.
Aug. 24/06

ALS Society of Canada
265 Yorkland Boulevard Suite 300
Toronto, Ontario
M2I 1S5

Dear Sir or Madam:

Re your letter for a donation to ALS Society.

The idea for a donation came from my daughter, ELIZABETH MURRAY, the letter was written out of spite. For proof you can write to my son Dr. Kevin Murray. Behind all this is a matter of hatred she has borne since I wouldn't turn the cottage at Falcon Lake over to her and never go down again. All of which she denies.

Explanation: I was sitting eating my breakfast at cottage (Falcon Lake) when and took my coffee to sit with her on the chesterfield by the front window, it was at this time she said I want you to turn the cottage over to me. Her husband Jeffry Hirsch was still in bed, shortly after a while she asked me to turn the cottage over to her and never go again, I refused - she then got up and went in the bedroom to tell Jeff - I went to the sink to wash the dishes etc.

Then they both came up to go out the door, stopped and turned to me and said they would never be down to the cottage again - ~~Davis their son who is now eleven~~ they bought a cottage of their own at Victoria Beach, possibly so they could contradict my statement re ~~cottage at Falcon Lake~~

By sending you a donation in my name I would say

it was spite more than anything else as I don't have
anything to do with her name. I did go down to their
cottage for 2 weeks but came home at the end of one ~~due
to the fact there were several spiteful little;~~

Re your request to donate to ALS. I don't know if it was
coincidental or not, but I have a daughter Elizabeth
Murray who is very spiteful towards me and thought up
the idea that I should send a donation to you

IT JUST OCCURRED TO ME WHEN I GOT HOME –
WHAT A DUMMY I WAS

Liz came over about noon, she ~~said~~ to see asked if
~~I wanted~~ she could take me over to renew my car
license - guess it was such a surprise I went along
with it - haven't talked to Liz for quite a while. ~~You see~~
Gail Zwarich had taken me ~~over at the end of~~ around -
at that time a man waited on me

I got my last drivers license in 2004 and asked to get it
renewed - he checked it over and approved - then asked
if I could come back the following week as ~~I would
have to have~~ they didn't have anyone to take me for a
drivers test.

Well Gail was called into work about the next day, so I
didn't know who to get to take me over so put it off until
she (Liz) came over yesterday - I was surprised but
didn't weigh it out - I agreed, she drove my car over
- not much talk but she was cheery -

~~There was~~ A girl was working and a few people
ahead of us - she was very nice and I told her I was

in about a month prior and had to have a road test - it was then she got all confused and kept looking at Liz who was slightly behind me, NEVER DAWNED ON ME - but after awhile she said I would have to try tests etc. to get my license - told her what was said before - never dawned on me what was happening -

- Liz was standing slightly behind me but claims she was sitting the whole time - she must have held that large sign (or big piece of cardboard) It had on it DEBENTURE or ALZHEIMERS because the girl's attitude changed so quickly. (this debenture business all started about 3 years ago)

Why do I think of these things too late - but such a difference in the reception I had when I went with Gail - the clerk or whoever was so ready to give me a road test

I SHOULD JUST BE ABLE TO RENEW MY DRIVERS PERMIT WENT OVER TO TO DRIVERS OFFICE - LIZ FOUND OUT ABOUT IT AND HELD SIGN UP - EARLY DEBENTURE SHE PUT POSTERS ALL OVER WHERE YOU RENEW PERMIT SAYING I HAVE DEBENTURE SO ANYONE CAN SEE THAT WHEN I TRY FOR MY DRIVERS EXAM

<u>Talk to Kevin</u>

When I came home today there were 2 xeroxed pages re Transportation and Government Services - one was <u>Notice of Suspension Section 28 (3) of the Highway Traffic Act</u> (read part of it to Kevin) the other was medical records "we have received the medical report completed on your behalf" (read rest of it from paper)

    these were in the mailbox today

    The letter was originally signed by the SUPERVISOR OF MEDICAL RECORDS - these medical records must have been made up by Kalansky - but can't figure out why I'm getting copies of them now

Liz must have left them just to prove her point that I'll never drive again - it was Liz who got me to go to Kalansky in the first place and the two of them have kept this up

Canadian Profession Police Assn.
253 College St
Box 157
Toronto, Ont.
M5J 1R5

Dear Sir:

I am surmising you have all the information regarding my reason for calling on the Police. I had my license taken away from me in Nov. 2004 originally instigated by my daughter and a Doctor friend of hers for spite - not giving her her own way, re my cottage its a long story

The doctor came up with Early Debenture as an excuse, not too long ago my daughter told me I would never drive again, here or in Ontario, same old phrase, - also a card   about 2 weeks ago copies of 2 letters were put in my mailbox to remind me of the medical records with a small notice attached to it - there was a copy of the suspension letter sent Nov 4/2004 from Transportation and Government Services not signed, but I was thinking of reporting same to Police to investigate the writing.

Also had a letter from Police office in Toronto? Something to do with police association. Sent a cheque for $50.00

WAS NOT KALANSKY
WHO WROTE THE LETTER RE HAVING
EARLY DEBENTURE — LAST TIME
I WENT TO HER WAS AUG 5TH 2005 OR
SIX BUT HAVE FOUND
OUT IT WAS ALL LIZ'S DOING —
JUST LIKE SHE STOPPED ME FROM
DRIVING, OF COURSE THAT'S
  BECAUSE I WOULDN'T GIVE HER THE
  COTTAGE — THEN DON'T KNOW
  HOW SHE FOUND OUT I WAS AT
  NEILS FOR XMAS AND WHEN
SARA BROUGHT ME HOME, CAME
IN AND SAW THE BOX OF
  LITTLE DOLLS IN THE HALLWAY
  TO GIVE TO ANGLICAN CHURCH
  AS THERE ARE A LOT OF PEOPLE COME FOR FOOD
  EVERYDAY AND CLOTHING
LIZ CAME AND WAS ABSOLUTELY FURIOUS
  AND TOOK A LOT OUT OF THE CABINET
  CLAIMING SHE BOUGHT ALL THOSE —
  HOWEVER I STILL
  HAD A COUPLE LARGE DOLLS ON A SHELF
  IN THE BASEMENT — PLUS ONE IN KEVIN'S OLD ROOM
—
WOULD LIKE TO SEND THOSE TO KEVIN FOR HIS
DAUGHTER — MAYBE I COULD PUT THEM ALL
IN A LARGE SUITCASE AND SEND THEM UP
WITH SOMEONE —
  EITHER WAY I WILL GET RID OF THEM
  BEFORE I MOVE. COULD BE MORE IN THE ATTIC —
  TOO COLD TO GO IN NOW

# Chapter Fifteen

**GREAT EXPECTATIONS, CHARLES** Dickens' nineteenth century tale about love and rejection, contains one of my favourite literary characters. Miss Havisham, an aging spinster who was jilted on her wedding day, never removed her white dress and stopped all the clocks in her ruined mansion to suspend the passage of time. As my mother's health continued to deteriorate, I wished that I could do the same – stop time and hold off her inevitable decline forever.

Communication had been a challenge ever since I had retrieved my dolls in late December. Instead of being able to monitor my mother's condition on my own, I was forced to rely more and more heavily on information from Daryl Dyck, Muriel Zwarich and my cousin, Carol. I was constantly worried that my mother wasn't receiving the care she needed.

When Jeff, Davis, and I were away for a few days at the end of March, Daryl Dyck arranged for a community health nurse to conduct a home visit to examine sores on my mother's leg that had developed as a result of her poor circulation. When we returned, there was a phone message from the nurse advising that there was water leaking into my mother's basement from a window well. In the background, I could hear my mother instructing the nurse what she ought to tell me.

The next morning I called to see how we could help. My mother responded in an aggressive tone.

"How do you know I have water in my basement?"

I reminded her about the nurse's message.

"I didn't have anyone call you," she said. "What good would it do to call you?" She eventually agreed that Jeff could come over and inspect the problem.

The window well was easily fixed. An accumulation of leaves and other debris had prevented the water from draining into the weeping tiles, and a wet-dry vacuum took care of the soggy carpet in the basement. We had no ready solution for what Jeff and I recognized as a significant worsening in my mother's cognitive function, and a corresponding increase in her paranoia. Our concerns were only confirmed by what happened next.

```
From:     "evmurray"
To:       "ddyck"
Sent:     April 22, 2007 8:31 PM
Subject:  Ellen Murray

Hi Daryl,
We had another situation with my mother this weekend.
On Friday afternoon, she telephoned to ask if Jeff and
I could come to her house that evening as there was
something she needed to discuss. When I pressed her for
more information, she said she had found a chair from her
sun porch underneath her kitchen window and was worried
that someone had tried to break into her house during the
night. I offered to come over right away but she said she
would rather wait until Jeff and I could come together.
When we arrived that evening she told us a bizarre story
that involved my cousin, Doug, her late brother's son.
Doug has been living in Winnipeg for many years but hasn't
been in contact with our family. He recently called my
mother and wanted to "reconnect."
My mother told us that Doug had been over either Wednesday
or Thursday. She said that "one minute" he was beside her
and the "next minute" she found him trying to remove a
window in the sun porch. She asked him what he was doing
and he told her that he wanted "access to her house." She
told him to stop but was "too astonished" to question him
any further. She was adamant that the chair hadn't been
in the back yard earlier in the week and concluded that
Doug had returned Thursday night to break into the house.
She then told us that Doug had come over on an earlier
occasion and suggested they go for a drive to Falcon Lake.
She said she was surprised Doug could find her cottage and
speculated that he had been staying there without her
knowledge. While they were there, Doug went down to the
dock to look at the water. She said she was glad she had
refused to go with him, as he had probably wanted to push
her in.
At my mother's request, Jeff called Doug and asked him what
he had been doing in my mother's sun porch. Jeff told him
that my mother believed he was trying to get access to her
house and that she was uncomfortable and scared. Doug was
surprised to hear her concerns. He said that they had gone
to her cottage last Saturday, and when they returned my
mother claimed she had lost her keys. Together they tried
```

to get into the house through a window in the sun porch for a couple of hours before my mother discovered the keys in her pocket. He explained that it had been my mother's idea to take the chair to the back yard to see if they could get in through the kitchen window rather than the sun porch. Jeff then called my mother and told her about his conversation with Doug. She denied Doug's version of events and called back four times that evening to reiterate her version of what had happened. She said that she couldn't understand why Doug would "make up a story" and she was nervous he might try to contact her. Jeff assured my mother several times that Doug had agreed to stay away from her.

On Saturday morning, my mother called and complained that Doug was at her house. She said he wouldn't go away even though she had refused to answer the door. Jeff reminded my mother that he had spoken to my cousin the previous night and that Doug had promised not to come by. She insisted that Doug was sitting in his car in her driveway but when Jeff arrived at my mother's house there was no one there. For the record, we believe Doug's version of the events. Jeff and I are very disturbed by my mother's stories and would like to meet with you to discuss our concerns.

I look forward to hearing from you at your earliest convenience. Thank you again for helping us deal with this difficult matter.

Liz Murray

From:     "evmurray"
To:       "ddyck"
Sent:     April 22, 2007 9:52 PM
Subject:  Ellen Murray

Hi Daryl,

Just an update to my previous email…

My mother telephoned this evening and said that Doug's car was parked on the street in front of her house. She said he had knocked on the door but she hadn't answered. I asked her if she would like Jeff to talk to Doug again. She agreed and Jeff made the call.

Doug said that he hadn't been at my mother's house since he last spoke to Jeff and wouldn't be going there any time soon. While Jeff was on the phone, my mother called back and left a message saying Doug was now parked in front of the neighbour's house. In a second message she insisted that she was still watching Doug's car from her bedroom window. When I finally connected with her she refused to believe that my cousin wasn't there. She was angry that I wouldn't "do something" and said she "didn't know where else to turn."

```
I'm hoping she doesn't decide to call the police.
Liz
```

Daryl must have sensed the underlying panic in my message or perhaps he was also becoming more concerned about my mother's situation. He called me before lunch the next day and scheduled a time for Jeff and me to meet with him and the attending geriatrician with the Riverview geriatric outpatient program.

I had accepted that my mother had dementia but the idea of the specialist making it official was still upsetting. As I drove to my mother's house two days before the meeting, I wasn't sure whether I was hoping to find more evidence to confirm that it was no longer safe for my mother to continue living on her own or whether I wanted to be persuaded that she was able to manage for at least a while longer.

My mother's front door was unlocked. I could smell the acrid odour of something burning and ran to the kitchen where a small pot of milk was boiling over on the stove. I turned off the stove and removed the pot from the black ring of scorched liquid that circled the burner.

"Mom?" I called.

Hot milk was my mother's bedtime drink. Hopefully, she hadn't forgotten the pot and gone to bed. I heard footsteps on the basement stairs and my mother appeared in the doorway of the kitchen. She stared in amazement at the ruined pot in the sink. She pursed her lips and frowned when I told her how it came to be there.

"Everyone forgets things sometimes," she said.

We both fell silent.

"I've decided I'm moving home," she finally declared. "I'm going to be gone by June first at the latest."

"Where exactly, are you planning to live?" I asked cautiously. I knew that her plan was never going to be executed but I couldn't help probing for the details of her imagined move.

"Miriam and Peter are on the lookout for some land for me to buy," my mother replied. "Of course they think I should be up by them in Hastings but I told them if I'm moving back, I'm moving to Campbellford."

"What kind of land are you thinking you want to buy?"

I tried to hide my incredulity.

"Oh, you know, just a plot of land big enough to build a house. I'm going to take the plan of this house and build the very same thing in Campbellford."

"You remember Miriam and Peter, don't you?" she continued. "I introduced them, you know. It was during the war, and Peter just turned up in town one day. He'd walked all across Canada and his feet were raw and bleeding. You remember – he's Japanese – his family had been put in some sort of camp out in British Columbia but he escaped and made his way to Campbellford. We got along right away but I knew Miriam was looking for a boyfriend, so I got the two of them together."

I had listened to my mother's stories enough times to know that what she had said was not true. Peter was Miriam's second husband. Her first husband, Charlie Shaw, had died suddenly about twenty-five years ago; my mother and I had gone to Ontario for the funeral. Miriam had met Peter fifteen years earlier when he retired from his job as a high school principal and moved from Toronto to just outside Campbellford. They were in the same bowling league and Peter had pursued Miriam for a long time before she agreed to go out with a younger man.

"That Winstanley boy was around again this morning," my mother said, referring to my cousin, Doug. "I didn't let him in when he rang the bell, but then he went and parked his car in front of the Gillespie house. I almost called the police since there was no answer at your place."

The next day, Jeff and I met with Daryl and Dr. Diane Blakely, the geriatrician at Riverview Day Hospital. The facility offered geriatric day programs as well as assessments and treatments by a range of professionals including nurses, occupational therapists, social workers, and physicians.

After a brief tour, we settled in a small conference room to discuss my mother's situation. I was feeling strangely nervous and a little defensive, as if we had been called into the headmaster's office at Davis' school to discuss an episode of bad behaviour. Dr. Blakely was soft-spoken and made me feel at ease almost immediately.

"I've discussed your mother's situation extensively with Daryl, in addition to reviewing the information you've provided." She paused briefly and smiled. "I know it's difficult but you're right to be concerned. Your mother is clearly exhibiting serious cognitive impairment."

I breathed a sigh of relief, somehow less burdened because she had given validation and an implicit offer of support without a negative judgment of my mother.

Jeff and I spent almost an hour describing our concerns. Daryl shared his observations from his visits with my mother and the results of the mini cognitive tests he had performed. Dr. Blakely explained that dementia is often incorrectly called senility and that people often believe serious mental decline is a normal part of aging. She said dementia describes a wide range of symptoms associated with a decline in cognitive functioning severe enough to interfere with daily life. My mother had dementia but Dr. Blakely couldn't say for sure if it was Alzheimer's disease, a common type of dementia. That could only be determined if my mother had additional neurological tests. My mother's case was unusual, she added, because my mother had the ability to manipulate her environment and, in limited circumstances, to present as a person who doesn't have a significant cognitive impairment. At the end of the meeting, we all agreed that something would have to be done in the near future.

Since my mother hadn't given anyone her Power of Attorney and wouldn't voluntarily seek assistance with her finances or change her living accommodations, we had only two options. I could apply to the Court to be appointed the committee of both my mother's person and property, or I could ask the Public Trustee to make a similar application.

In the first instance, my name would be prominent as the applicant in the court documents – which would inevitably create a problem when the documents were served on my mother, as they had to be. In addition, two physicians would have to certify that my mother wasn't mentally competent. Dr. Blakely would be one and she would do a home visit if necessary, but getting my mother to see a second doctor would be problematic.

On the other hand, if the Public Trustee applied to be my mother's committee, only one physician's report would be necessary. That would make the application considerably easier, but I wasn't sure if I was comfortable with a government official deciding what was in my mother's best interests. If the Public Trustee was prepared to take direction from me, on the understanding that I would make a subsequent application to take over as committee after we had my mother settled in a different living arrangement, that might be the best solution. We weren't sure what an appropriate living arrangement would be and I certainly didn't want the Public Trustee to make that determination.

Jeff and I left the meeting with a lot to think about. The options weren't difficult conceptually, but emotionally the decision seemed enormous. Even with diminished capacity, my mother would have some understanding of the copy of the court order she would receive, albeit with her own interpretation of its meaning and effect. Before the onset of her illness, I knew that she would have been humiliated by the thought of what was going to happen to her, no matter which option I pursued.

In the days that followed, Daryl and I developed a plan that would move us closer to our ultimate goal of having my mother under the care of a committee without initiating the formal proceedings. We decided that Daryl would persuade my mother to visit Riverview Day Hospital on May seventeenth, ostensibly to allow a nurse to examine and treat the sores that had resulted from the poor circulation in her leg. Once at the hospital, she would also be seen by Dr. Blakely for a standard geriatric assessment, as well as by an occupational therapist for supplementary cognitive testing. Our hope was that my mother would then agree to return to the hospital on a weekly basis for ongoing assessment and evaluation, which would give me time to decide how I wanted the court application to proceed.

To ensure that all of the professionals who would be seeing my mother had as much information as possible, I prepared a seventeen-page narrative that described the evolution of my mother's growing paranoia and decreased cognitive function. I sent a copy of the document to Daryl and another to Kevin, asking him to contribute similar information. A decision was going to have to be made and I didn't want to make it alone.

Kevin didn't respond with the details of his own concerns about my mother. Instead, he asked whether I was keeping Neil informed. I had left a message when the incident with my cousin Doug first occurred but Neil had been away and it hadn't been a priority to contact him again. Hoping to placate Kevin and garner his cooperation, I picked up the telephone.

"So she's going to Riverview Day Hospital on the seventeenth for a general assessment to see where Dr. Blakely thinks she's at cognitively. I've prepared a summary of my concerns so she knows some of the background. I'll send you a copy, and then if you write out your concerns for me to send along as well, it would really help," I told Neil, after I recounted the Doug story in detail.

"Kevin and I agree that Mom can't go on living in her house," he replied. "Send me what you've done and I'll have a look."

A few days before May seventeenth, Daryl presented me with a new problem.

"Last week your Mom agreed to go to Riverview to have her leg looked at. But when I was there again today, she said she wouldn't go. I'll see her once more before the seventeenth to try and get her back on track."

Daryl's news upset me enough to call Kevin. May seventeenth was the Thursday before the Victoria Day long weekend and I knew he would be coming to open his cottage. I hoped he could come a day or two early and help me get my mother to her assessment.

"I'm coming in Thursday night," Kevin told me. "I've got patients booked during the day. The appointments are set weeks in advance."

I felt like the little red hen that asked the other farm animals for assistance as she harvested wheat and made it into bread. *Who will help me get Mom the care she needs?*

Neil phoned me first thing in the morning on Friday, the eighteenth of May.

"Did Mom get to Riverview yesterday for her assessment?" he asked.

"Did Kevin come in?" I asked instead.

"He's coming in this weekend," Neil replied.

"Didn't he come in last night?" I countered.

Neil paused.

"Oh yes, he did."

"And isn't he staying with you?"

"Yes, he is," Neil agreed.

In my mind, Kevin should have called me rather than Neil. I felt like hanging up. Instead, I told Neil that Mom had been extremely defensive and Dr. Blakely had only been able to conduct limited cognitive testing.

"Based on general memory tests and her discussion with Mom, she saw definite cognitive impairment," I said. "Dr. Blakely was also concerned about the circulation in Mom's leg and ordered further tests. The goal is to have her return on a weekly basis for in depth cognitive testing and to monitor her leg."

I ended by saying that I had not yet received a report from the occupational therapist but that I would speak to Daryl Dyck the following week to obtain more detailed information about the visit and the proposed plan for ongoing contact.

Perhaps I wasn't being fair to Neil but I had never thought that my mother should be his responsibility. Since I wasn't interested in communicating with him simply as a conduit for passing information to Kevin, I thought about whether I should forgo initiating any further contact with Kevin unless he contacted me directly. In the end, I decided that continuing communication was in my mother's best interests.

```
From:     "evmurray"
To:       "Kevin Murray"
Sent:     May 22, 2007   9:33 AM
Subject:  Ellen Murray

Hi Kevin,
As Neil probably told you, I had a brief discussion with
Dr. Blakely following Mom's assessment last Thursday. At
the time we spoke Mom hadn't yet met with the occupational
therapist, nor had she completed all of the scheduled
testing. Hopefully Mom will cooperate and agree to return
to Riverview on a regular basis for observation and further
testing.
In the meantime, Dr. Blakely, Daryl Dyck, Jeff and I
agree that Mom can't continue to live independently much
longer. In order to move her — since it is unlikely she'll
agree —either I'll need to be appointed committee or the
Public Trustee will. Mom will have to be served with
court documents either way, which will undoubtedly upset
her, so I don't want to proceed with either application
until we've decided that the move is absolutely necessary.
At the moment, I'm comfortable (more or less) with Mom
remaining in the house for the summer but I don't think
she should stay there another winter. Dr. Blakely seems to
be in agreement with this approach provided the situation
doesn't deteriorate. In order to better assess what will
be best for Mom, I'm attempting to monitor her condition
and provide ongoing information to Daryl Dyck and Dr.
Blakely. Your input on this would be appreciated; it would
assist us in developing an appropriate plan. Since Mom was
with you at your cottage over the weekend, it would be
useful to have your comments with respect to her cognitive
functioning during that time.
Liz
```

I was almost too busy to care that Kevin didn't respond to my email. In addition to working with Daryl to organize my mother's follow-up visits to Riverview Day Hospital, I had spoken to two of her neighbours, Debbie Good and Odarka Trosky. Each recited several reasons that they were concerned about my mother. Debbie had seen her shovelling the driveway in the middle of winter wearing only a light sweater. Both women had spotted her driving her car. I knew my mother had kept her car in working order but it hadn't occurred to me that she would drive without a valid license. I was angry with myself for being so naïve.

A telephone call to the police confirmed that they wouldn't impound my mother's car even if she were caught driving. Jeff and I knew that she wouldn't let us take the vehicle without a fight so our only hope was to disable it. Our mechanic suggested that disconnecting the fuel pump would be an easy, efficient method.

When we arrived at my mother's house to carry out the deed, there was a silver Toyota parked in her driveway.

"Someone's here," my mother whispered to us when she finally came to the door. "She arrived just I got home from the store. Come and see if you know who she is."

My cousin was sitting at the kitchen table. Cathy Murray hadn't been a regular visitor even when our fathers were alive, but except for a few lines around her eyes and a few streaks of grey in her short, brown hair, Cathy's appearance hadn't changed in twenty-five years.

"Hey, Cathy," I said. "What brings you here?"

I sat across from her while my mother returned to her chair at the head of the table. Jeff stood by the stairs leading to the family room and the door to the garage, waiting for an opportunity to slip away and undertake his mission.

"I was looking at an apartment near here," she replied. "It made me wonder if your mother was still in the neighbourhood."

Empty coffee mugs and a half-eaten plate of chocolate covered cookies indicated that Cathy hadn't just arrived. My mother sat sideways in her chair, one leg crossed over the other, swinging her top foot slowly. She reached for a cookie and then paused when it was halfway to her mouth.

"Now, what did you say your connection was?" she asked.

"I'm Angus' daughter, Cathy. Angus was your husband's brother."

Cathy spoke slowly. She caught my eye and raised her eyebrows. I gathered that this wasn't the first time she had explained the relationship.

"I never knew Angus had a daughter," my mother said, chewing her cookie reflectively. "I knew he had a son – or maybe two sons. But I never knew he had a daughter."

She looked at Cathy, clearly suspicious that she may not be telling the truth about her identity.

"Where are you working now?" I asked, changing the subject.

Cathy and I carried the conversation for the next half hour with occasional interruptions from my mother who wanted up-to-date information about Cathy's father, who had been dead for eighteen years. Cathy and I were both relieved when Jeff joined us, nodding his head in my direction to indicate that his job was done.

Cathy got up to leave and my mother told her to *be sure and drop by again*. When the screen door banged shut behind her, my mother turned to me with a quizzical look on her face.

"Who was that woman?" she asked.

The phone was ringing when Jeff and I arrived home a short time later.

"I know what you're up to," my mother said. Her voice was harsh. "You brought that woman here as a test so when I didn't know who she was you could tell everyone my mind is going."

She hung up before I could respond.

"What was that all about?" Jeff asked.

I was still holding the receiver in my hand.

"I'm not really sure," I replied.

I added the Cathy incident to my list of concerns for Daryl and Dr. Blakely to consider. I was still torn between thinking it was no longer safe for my mother to continue to live on her own, and knowing how much she was going to hate being forced into different accommodations. Since my mother wouldn't move out of her house voluntarily, an assisted living environment wasn't an option. Daryl and I had agreed that unless my mother was in secured housing, she would probably try and leave. That limited our choice to a nursing home, which seemed like such a drastic measure. I couldn't bear to think about my mother, who was still so capable physically, living in a nursing home.

"Wait and see how the follow-up visits to Riverview go," Jeff cautioned. "We need to know more about what Daryl and Dr. Blakely think before we make a final decision."

```
From:     "evmurray"
To:       "Kevin Murray"
Cc:       "nmurray"
Sent:     June 17, 2007 12:53 PM
Subject: Mom

Kevin,
As you will recall, after Mom's cognitive evaluation at
Riverview on May 17 the plan was for her to return for
further observation and testing.
On May 30, Mom was assessed by an occupational therapist
who reported as follows:
a.) Mom didn't know where she was, and was confused as to
the time of day, date, and year during the testing.
b.) Mom had a great deal of difficulty with the financial
aspects of the test. When she was given an envelope
with examples of documents she might have to deal with
(invoices, cheques, coupons, blank Visa Application etc.)
she was unable to properly determine what to do with
them. She didn't recognize a dollar coin and didn't know
how much it was worth (she thought it was the same as a
quarter). She wasn't able to fill in a cheque properly.
c.) Mom didn't demonstrate appropriate judgment in the
judgment section of the test.
d.) Mom had a great deal of difficulty focusing and was
easily distracted.
Her conclusion is that Mom has moderate to severe memory
and cognitive impairment.
Mom has refused to return to Riverview which means that
the ongoing cognitive evaluations we had contemplated
won't be happening.
On June 20, Dr. Blakely and Daryl Dyck will meet with the
occupational therapist and the nurse who examined Mom
on May 17. They will discuss Mom's case and determine a
recommended plan of action. Jeff and I will then be meeting
with the team. If you have an opinion with respect to Mom's
functioning and/or what you think would be in Mom's best
interests in terms of both her person and her property,
please provide me with your comments prior to June 20.
Liz
```

Kevin answered me later the next day. He indicated that his observations on the May long weekend were consistent with the occupational therapist's assessment and agreed that a nursing home, while far from an ideal solution, was the only real option. "Mom continues to threaten to hire a lawyer to get you out of her life once and for all, so it will be difficult for you to be her committee if you decide to take that on," he wrote.

```
From:      "evmurray"
To:        "Kevin Murray"
Cc:        "nmurray"
Sent:      June 27, 2007 8:37 PM
Subject:   Re: Mom
```

Kevin,
Jeff and I met with the Riverview team last Wednesday. All felt strongly that Mom wasn't able to continue to manage her finances or make decisions regarding her person (particularly with respect to her future living arrangements) on her own. Daryl Dyck and Dr. Blakely suggested that when I was ready to have Mom declared incompetent, the required cognitive assessment could be done on a home visit. This would eliminate the problem of persuading Mom to attend at Riverview. They suggested that they should initiate the process to have the Public Trustee appointed as committee of Mom's person and property and that I could then apply to take over as Mom's committee when appropriate. They felt this plan was the best option for two reasons. First, the application to the Public Trustee would only require one medical report, which Dr. Blakely would provide. Second, they hoped that if they initiated the process for the Public Trustee to become involved they would take the brunt of Mom's anger rather than me.
This is a very difficult decision for me to make. I've spent a lot of time during the last week trying to determine when I ought to give Daryl and Dr. Blakely the go ahead. If they're in agreement, I'm still inclined to give Mom one last summer in her house before we proceed. However, I'd like to know if you're okay with this decision before I communicate further with Daryl.
While Mom expresses hostility towards me, she also asks both Jeff and me for assistance. Her hostility is a result of her inability to accept her own deficiencies, her growing paranoia, and her reluctance to ask for help generally.

```
I understand that her attitude towards me won't improve
if I become her committee, regardless of the process by
which that is achieved. However, I have been primarily
responsible for Mom for many years, at her request and on
my own initiative, and I'm prepared to continue to look
after her to the best of my ability.
I hope to hear from you once you have read this email.
Liz
```

Kevin's response was to take the advice of the geriatrics team regarding the involvement of the Public Trustee. It was a pragmatic direction which addressed the intellectual problem of what to do but not the emotional issue of when to do it.

For the next few days, it seemed that everywhere I went – out for lunch, grocery shopping, walking the dog – I saw mothers and daughters enjoying their time together. Dementia had destroyed the camaraderie my mother and I had once shared, whispering invectives in her ear until all of our interactions were laced with tension. Instead of planning a joint activity, I was plotting to have her locked away in a nursing home. I wondered if my mother's accusations were right. Perhaps I was an awful daughter.

Finally, I took the easy way out and accepted Kevin's response as an endorsement of my plan to forgo any action until the fall when I would ask the Public Trustee to have my mother declared incompetent and then make my own application to become her committee. I was grateful for the reprieve but I still wasn't sure that I had made the right decision.

When I went over to Drivers station on St Marys road last fall was told as it was later on in the afternoon there weren't any drivers available to give me a test in my own car. Gail Zwarich drove me over that time.

Then Liz went over with me - hesitant at first to go with her as I know she just hated the thought of me ever driving again. She held up a sign that said debenture and I didn't get my license back. She is nasty and jealous because of the damn lake, me not giving her the cottage and never going down again. Will write about this and the rest in my book to be read out at my funeral - I'm going to let those I haven't already told know just what she is like

Liz why did you come over this afternoon just when I got home - and bring your friend who you have never mentioned to me, was it just to show her that I wouldn't remember her - after all a lot has happened since I went to Angus Murray's

At first I felt rather glad you had kept in touch with her, then I got wondering WHY NOW?? you know I think Jeff is far too good a person for you. When I think back on everything bad in my life well - I won't go into that - but go ahead and do all the dirty things you can - remember the fuss you made when Sara had come over after Xmas and saw all those dolls and took them away - the fuss you made

now when I called Neil a while ago he wouldn't speak to me - well he has had it as far as I'm concerned

Kevin-

Re Liz coming right after I got home from grocery shopping, she had Angus Murray's daughter with her - I hadn't forgotten he had one, but never remember her looks - she's grown up - must be years since I have seen or heard tell of her - but what gets me how did Liz and Jeff know when I was coming home? Think maybe she's been watching my house again. Jeff is always the same - too good for her.

# Chapter Sixteen

**THE LABOUR DAY** weekend is a time of beginnings and endings. Summer whites and sandals are replaced with chunky sweaters and boots. Sultry days turn cooler; leaves wither and gardens ripen. While other families settled into the familiar household routines of autumn, the weeks that loomed before me were uncharted territory. Davis would start his four-year journey through upper school. I would start the proceedings to have my mother declared incompetent and moved into a nursing home.

It was five minutes before ten o'clock on the Thursday evening before the August long weekend in 2007. The ring of the telephone interrupted my review of a summer's worth of mail and a quick glance at our call display made my heart and my imagination start to race.

"Hi, it's Debbie Good, your mother's neighbour," the caller said. "She's fine, don't worry, but I think you need to come right away."

"You're sure my mother's okay?"

I was always better dealing with an emergency than contemplating one.

"She's fine," Debbie repeated. "Just a little confused. She was out driving and got lost. But she's here now."

I told Debbie that I would be right over and she could tell me the whole story in person.

As Jeff and I pulled into my mother's driveway, Debbie was standing on her front step, waiting for us to arrive.

"Is she at home?" I asked Debbie, gesturing towards my mother's house.

Debbie shook her head and pointed to my mother's car parked in front of the Troskys' house two doors away. The front end of the car was two feet from the curb and its back end at least double that distance. My mother was sitting in the driver's seat, with Odarka Trosky next to her.

"She won't come out," Debbie explained.

"What happened?" I asked Debbie while Jeff started towards my mother's car.

"My husband and I had been out for a walk. We were just coming up our driveway when a man stopped us and said he was helping an elderly woman who had been waving down cars on University Crescent and asking if someone could show her the way home. She told the man she thought she lived at 38 Thatcher Drive, but then she didn't recognize the house. That's why she's parked in front of Odarka's."

"Thank God no one was hurt," I said, when Debbie paused to take a breath. I felt relieved, angry and afraid all at once. If anyone had been injured, it would have been my fault. It had been my decision to let my mother have one last summer in her house.

Debbie nodded emphatically. She dangled a set of keys in one hand.

"I'm not really sure how I did it, but your mother eventually handed over her keys. I didn't want to leave them with her, that's for sure. Then Odarka came out and said she'd sit with your mother while I called you. We tried to get her out of the car but she refused. She sure is stubborn, your mother."

The sound of a car door closing seemed unnaturally loud in the quiet neighbourhood. I looked over and saw Jeff leading my mother towards her house. His arm circled her shoulders, holding her steady as they walked together. She was wearing slippers and a short-sleeved shirt. As they passed beneath a streetlight, I could see that she was shivering.

"I don't understand how the car is working. I thought we'd taken care of that problem," I muttered.

"A CAA tow truck was at your mother's house the other day," Debbie offered. "I thought it was strange but I wasn't sure what was going on."

My mother sat in her favourite wing-backed chair, wrapped in the off-white cashmere throw we had given her for Christmas several years earlier. In better times, my mother had occupied that chair with the boldness of Wonderland's Queen of Hearts. Now the chair seemed gargantuan and my mother looked like a tiny Alice, unsure as to where she was and how she had come to be there. Her eyebrows were drawn together and her lips pursed as she tried to make sense of her situation.

"How did you know I was having coffee with Odarka Trosky?" she finally asked. "You couldn't see me in her kitchen from the street, could you?"

Jeff and I exchanged a look. I wasn't sure if she remembered what had happened or not, and Jeff was clearly wondering the same thing.

"You weren't in Odarka's house. Odarka was sitting with you in your car," I told her as gently as I could manage.

My mother pulled the throw tighter around her body and frowned. She didn't seem to notice that Jeff and I were watching her.

"Oh yes, that's right. I was just taking my car around the block to see if it still worked. It stalled in front of Odarka's house and she came out to help me get it going."

I opened my mouth to scold her for daring to drive even around the block but Jeff intervened.

"I'll take your car to the garage tomorrow and get it fixed, Mother-in-law," he said.

My mother's frown deepened as she considered her position. She wanted her car in working order but she didn't want to let it out of her sight. Jeff coughed to get my attention. He mouthed the word keys and raised his eyebrows. I nodded and pointed at my chest with my thumb. My mother was concentrating on her dilemma and didn't notice our exchange.

Jeff knew that if we waited too long, my mother was sure to come up with some reason for her car to remain with her, and we couldn't let that happen.

"Well, Mother-in-law, I've got an early day tomorrow," he said firmly. "So we're going to have to get going."


DARYL DYCK HAD moved to a new position over the summer but his replacement, Sande Kliewer, had proved to be equally helpful. At eight o'clock Friday morning, I called Sande and told her about my mother's latest adventure.

Sande agreed that it was time to put our plan in motion and arrange for Dr. Blakely to conduct a formal cognitive assessment of my mother. I emailed Kevin and Neil with an update of my mother's activities as well as a synopsis of my conversation with Sande. My message concluded with a familiar request.

*I would welcome any comments or concerns you have with respect to how we are proposing to proceed. I assume you will consent to my application for committee when that process is initiated.*

Kevin's return message was a brief acknowledgment that it was wonderful no one was hurt. Neil called me almost immediately.

"Barb and I haven't seen Mom much lately," he said. "But Kevin had some trouble with her over the summer."

"What kind of trouble?" I asked.

"He took her out to his cottage for a few days but as soon as they got there Mom wanted to go to her own place. When Kevin said he was going sailing she got mad and ran away. It was a while before they found her. Kevin was pretty worried."

I hung up the telephone, wishing I had learned that information sooner.

Late Tuesday morning, the telephone rang just as I was gathering my courage to call Sande Kliewer to ask if she had spoken with Dr. Blakely.

"Guess who just called me?"

Jeff's voice was tense.

"Don't keep me waiting," I told him.

"A police officer. Apparently your mother told him that I stole her car."

I started to laugh.

"What did he say?"

"He asked me if I had my mother-in-law's car." Jeff wasn't amused. "I told him that I certainly did and I wasn't giving it back, either. When I explained why, he told me he understood my position and wouldn't be pursuing the matter. He told me to have a nice day."

I could tell Jeff was smiling now.

"Liz, you've got to call Sande Kliewer and make sure things are moving. You can't wait any longer."

```
From:    "evmurray"
To:      "Kevin Murray"
Cc:      "Jeff Hirsch"
Sent:    September 8, 2007 8:10 PM
Subject: Mom
```

Kevin,
Dr. Blakely saw Mom on Thursday evening and conducted a formal cognitive evaluation. As expected, her conclusion is that Mom is not competent to manage her property or her personal affairs. When I told her I was feeling conflicted about having a committee appointed she insisted that Mom has been at risk for some time and that it's now necessary to proceed.
Here's what happens next.
Dr. Blakely will submit a Certificate of Incapacity to the Director of Psychiatric Services for the Province of Manitoba.
The Director will issue a Notice of Intent indicating that the Public Trustee will become Mom's committee unless a written objection is filed within ten days. A copy of the Notice will be mailed to Mom as well as to you and me as her closest relatives. (Neil will not be notified since he doesn't have a legal relationship with Mom.)
If Mom manages to file an objection, which I don't think she will, the Chief Psychiatrist of Manitoba will contact her to determine if her objection is valid. Assuming that doesn't happen, the Public Trustee could become Mom's committee in as little as two weeks after the Notice of Intent is issued.
As soon as the Public Trustee is committee, an application to have Mom panelled for a nursing home will be submitted to the long term care review board. All of the preliminary interviews will be done in the next two weeks so that the application is ready when the PT is in place. Since it could be dangerous for Mom to remain at home after she receives the Notice of Intent (who knows what she will do), Sande Kliewer will ask the long term care review board to designate her application "community urgent." This means that she would have priority placement in the nursing homes on the community urgent list. There are a limited number of homes on that list at any time so we won't have much choice about where Mom is placed initially but she can be moved at a later date. I'm planning to visit Tuxedo Villa and West Park Manor next week. Those

will likely be my first two choices given their convenient locations and I am hoping that at least one of them will be on the community urgent list.

At some point after the Public Trustee is appointed, I will make my application to become committee. I will be forwarding a Consent by email for you to execute in due course (it will have to be witnessed by a lawyer or Notary Public).

If you have any questions or concerns please let me know.
Liz


From:      "evmurray"
To:        "Kevin Murray"
Cc:        "Jeff Hirsch"
Sent:      September 9, 2007 9:49 PM
Subject: Re: Mom

Kevin,

I have discussed the issue of managing Mom's property with the Public Trustee. She has agreed that it probably won't be necessary for her office to take charge of Mom's assets provided I proceed with my committee application in a timely fashion.

When I become committee I will assume control of Mom's person and property. I will be required to identify all of Mom's assets and file an inventory with the court. I will also be required to pass accounts through the court on a regular basis (probably annually) to assure there is no wrongdoing. As committee, I'll have to obtain court approval for any disposition of real property. I'll have to obtain accounting and legal (estate planning) advice from time to time and a financial plan will have to be developed when it is obvious what Mom's ongoing expenses will be.

You should be aware that Mom signed a listing agreement for the cottage on Wednesday. Luckily the real estate agent was concerned about Mom's competency and called me after the agreement was signed. I told him not to proceed with the listing.

This afternoon Mom called me and told me she had had a nap and woke up feeling happier than she had felt for a long time. She asked me to come over for a visit and said that she wanted to take Jeff, Davis, and me out for dinner. This was in stark contrast to my visit on Friday, where she met me at the door, told me I had ruined her life and said that she wanted nothing more to do with me.
Liz

Jeff and I were on high alert. The Chief Psychiatrist of Manitoba had received Dr. Blakely's report and had agreed that my mother was incompetent. A Notice of Intent advising my mother of the decision had been sent in the mail and we were anticipating the inevitable fall out.

I did my best to visit and call regularly so I would know when the letter arrived but in the end, it was Kevin who alerted me by email on September fourteenth that my mother had received the notice. His message indicated that she was angry and thought he and I were somehow *in cahoots*. He warned me that she might do something foolish and suggested I pay her a visit.

I was happy that Kevin had advised me that the notice had arrived, but before I went to see my mother I wanted more information about her reaction. I called Kevin at his home.

"I talked to Neil and asked him to check on Mom," he told me. "By the way, I'm not going to agree that you should be Mom's committee."

"What do you mean?" I asked. "All along the plan has been that I would apply to be committee."

"I know," Kevin replied. He cleared his throat. "But I've decided I want to be involved too."

My head was spinning. I wanted to get off the telephone and see what was happening at my mother's house.

"Look," I finally said after a moment or two of silence. "I'm going to have to think about this. And I don't even know if the legislation provides for joint committees. It may not be possible."

Jeff had heard a one-sided version of my conversation with Kevin. I filled him in on the details that he had missed as we drove to Thatcher Drive.

"He thinks we should be joint committees," I ranted. "He thinks we can make decisions together. Does he realize that would entail regular communication? That he would have to respond to my messages in a timely fashion, not just if and when he feels like it? That he might even have to talk to me on the phone once in a while? And why is he doing this now? Doesn't he realize how much we're dealing with here?" I was working myself into a fury. "And WHY would he call Neil and just e-mail me?"

"Let's take care of your mother for now. We'll take care of Kevin later," Jeff told me.

Jeff didn't get angry often but now his mouth was drawn into a firm line.

Neil and Barb were sitting in the living room with my mother when Jeff and I arrived. My mother was huddled in a chair by the fireplace. The flannelette pajamas she was wearing were once a rosy pink but now had only a faint blush of color. Her hair was flattened on one side; her eyes were so swollen they appeared only half open. One of her arms was wrapped around her waist; the other held a crumpled tissue to her mouth. My mother wasn't crying but it hadn't been long since she had been. Both Neil and Barb looked relieved when we entered the room.

"She was sleeping when we got here about forty-five minutes ago," Neil told us in a voice that reflected the strain of the evening. "We got her out of bed."

"Have you heard, Liz?" my mother asked. "The government is going to take away all my property. They want everything I have."

Her lips quivered. The rage Kevin had described had clearly been spent.

Neil raised his eyebrows and handed me a document that had been resting on the coffee table in front of him. I read it quickly; the word *incompetent* blurred and my hand shook as I passed it along to Jeff. As I had expected, it was the Notice from the Chief Psychiatrist. Absent an appeal, in ten days the Public Trustee would become legally responsible for my mother. The paper was badly wrinkled, as if it had been crumpled into a tiny ball and then straightened.

My mother wiped her runny nose with her tissue.

"They even want this house. They're going to take my house and put me in a home for the aged."

Although the Notice didn't say anything about moving my mother out of her house and into a nursing home, her fears were accurate. That process would soon be initiated. My mother was looking at me, judging my reaction to what she had said. I wasn't going to lie to her, but I wasn't going to tell her the whole truth, either.

"That's not what it says here, Mom. This just says that the Public Trustee is going to be in control. Everything will still be yours."

"But I want to be in charge of my own things. I can take care of myself. You know that. Isn't there something you can do?" She turned to Jeff. "You're a lawyer. Can't you help me?" A tear escaped from her eye and rested on her cheek.

Jeff chose his words carefully.

"We can look at the options, Mother-in-law. You know we want what's best for you."

Jeff and I spent the next hour sharing small talk with Neil and Barb. My mother sat quietly, eyes glazed, lost in her own fears. Every once in a while she would ask why the government wanted her property, or tell us that she was fine living on her own and that she cleaned her house from top to bottom twice a week. Neil shook his head and muttered *I don't know* to everything my mother said, looking to Jeff and me for guidance. The platitudes we offered were only modestly more informative, and probably no more comforting. When it became apparent that my mother was exhausted from the emotional turmoil of the day and was struggling to keep awake, we all made our exit. Barb squeezed my mother's arm as she left and told her that they would be back to see her soon.

The next day, in between morning and evening visits with my mother, I called a lawyer who specialized in guardianship and estate matters. I explained that my mother was suffering from dementia and outlined the plan we had constructed with Daryl Dyck and Dr. Blakely, whereby the Public Trustee would become my mother's committee and I would then initiate an application to take over that role. I told the lawyer that my brother didn't live in Manitoba, that we didn't get along, and that he had developed a last-minute scheme whereby we would share the responsibilities of committee jointly.

"Where do I stand?" I asked her. "Are joint committees even allowed?"

"There can be joint committees," she confirmed. "But a committee must be a resident of Manitoba. *The Mental Health Act* is very clear on that point. In fact, it was recently amended specifically to include that provision."

As the lawyer spoke in her calm, sensible voice, I began to cry. I was feeling so stressed and miserable about the process that the prospect of a scuffle with Kevin was just too much for me to contemplate. While Kevin might have had as great a moral right as I had to be my mother's committee, I was grateful that the legislation didn't allow him the opportunity.

Kevin didn't see things the same way. When I called him Sunday evening to report on my mother's weekend and share my lawyer's comments, he was unconvinced.

"I'll look into it myself," he said.

Two weeks of uncertainty followed our conversation. Kevin spoke to one of his close friends in Winnipeg, a lawyer who didn't specialize in the relevant area of the law. Armed with his friend's assurance that he could be a joint committee, Kevin maintained his position. The stress of dealing with Kevin at the same time as I was trying to care for my mother was crushing. I became so agitated by his refusal to listen to reason that I was willing to do almost anything to reach a resolution. I even contemplated forgoing my plan to become my mother's committee – and if that hadn't meant that the Public Trustee would be in control of every aspect of my mother's life, including where she would live and what medical treatment she would receive, I would have done so.

```
From:     "evmurray"
To:       "Kevin Murray"
Sent:     September 18, 2007  4:05 PM
Subject:  Mom

Kevin,
I really don't want to fight with you about the committee
business or anything else. I am heartsick about what has
happened to Mom over the last several years as well as what
```

is happening now. I don't know if it is possible for our
relationship to improve but I hope we can work together to
deal with what has to be dealt with vis a vis Mom. Maybe
it's time to try and mend some of our differences.
Life is too short.
Liz

Kevin replied that he thought we both wanted to help Mom enjoy the
best quality of life that she could. Nevertheless, he continued to insist that
we apply to be joint committees. In his opinion, the provisions of *The Mental
Health Act* that prohibited an out of province committee were open to a court
challenge.

I spent a few days thinking about how I should respond. I could
understand Kevin's desire to be involved but it simply wasn't possible under
the legislation.

From:      "evmurray"
To:        "Kevin Murray"
Sent:      September 21, 2007  9:05 AM
Subject: Mom

Kevin,
You are not entitled to be a joint committee under the
definition of committee in The  Mental Health Act. If
you were entitled, I would gladly agree. But I will not
be involved in an application to challenge the current
legislation. Not only would it be expensive, time-
consuming, and emotionally draining, I believe it would
also be unsuccessful. As a result, I intend to pursue an
application to be Mom's committee with or without your
consent.
After I am appointed committee, I would be happy to go
through Mom's financial papers with you and Neil.
Liz

By the last weekend of September, I was still waiting for Kevin to tell
me his final position regarding my application for committee. I didn't know
that Kevin was in Winnipeg to close his cottage for the winter, and to see my
mother. I learned of his visit when I arrived at my mother's house on Sunday
afternoon. Kevin and his twelve-year-old son, Graeme, along with Neil and

Barb, were sitting in the living room.

With all of the seating already occupied – Neil and Barb on the couch, my mother and Kevin on the matching wingback chairs, and Graeme on the remaining chair – I settled myself on the stairs that led from the living room to the second floor. Neil, who was positioned nearest the stairs, leaned over the arm of the couch and spoke sotto voce.

"Barb and I picked Kevin and Graeme up from the airport on Friday night and brought them here to see Mom. We went through that file box in her bedroom. Did you know she has stock certificates in there?"

"No, I didn't," I said. "I've never looked at her private papers."

I didn't point out that given my mother's attitude towards me it was unlikely she would have allowed it.

The conversation that followed was strained and uncomfortable. My mother would often interject a comment about the proceedings by the Public Trustee.

"The government can't just take all my property, can it?" she asked at one point.

Since I had answered the same question, or a variation of it, multiple times in the preceding two weeks, I remained silent, waiting for Neil or Kevin to try his hand at calming her fear. Graeme was the only one who rose to the task.

"Well, Grandma," he said. "It probably can. The government can do whatever it wants."

I bit the inside of my cheek and forced away a smile. Graeme's response reinforced my mother's belief about the Public Trustee's intentions, and she looked at him as if she was assessing his potential as an ally in the fight. Graeme was oblivious to both of our reactions.

Kevin finally looked at his watch, cleared his throat and announced that it was time for him to leave. All of us stood and, one by one, said our good-byes to my mother. Tears filled her eyes as Kevin put on his shoes in the front hall.

"I probably won't be here the next time you come," she said.

None of us disagreed.

I followed Kevin's car up the street. He pulled over to the side of the road when we were out of sight of my mother's house. I got out of my car as he started walking back to where I was parked.

"I'm still waiting to talk to the Public Trustee," was his opening statement.

"That's fine," I replied. "You'll be served with my application next week. You can consent or not."

Kevin cleared his throat again.

"It looks like Mom does have a Will."

For years my mother had refused to prepare a Will. *Maybe someday* was her typical response to the suggestion.

"Oh?" I said, thinking, *what about my committee application?* "Did you find it when you were looking through her papers?"

He shifted from one foot to the other.

"No, but I found a letter from a lawyer."

"Oh?" I said again. "Who's the lawyer?"

"I don't remember. But his office was on Portage Avenue."

"Well, I guess we can cross that bridge when we come to it," I said.


On the twenty-fifth of September, the ten-day appeal period described in the Chief Psychiatrist's letter had expired. My mother was officially incompetent and under the care of the Public Trustee. While we waited for the inevitable paperwork to be completed at the Public Trustee's office, Jeff and I spoke with Sande Kliewer about initiating the process to have my mother assessed and paneled for a nursing home. Officially we would have to wait for instructions from whoever was assigned my mother's file in the Public Trustee's office, but in light of my intention to take control as soon as possible, we anticipated that person would follow our lead. Thankfully, I had one less thing to worry about since Kevin had abandoned his fight to be appointed joint committee after hearing that the Public Trustee would oppose his application.

For the uninitiated, navigating the process of having a loved one placed in a nursing home can be a formidable task. Jeff and I were uninitiated. Sande explained that the Winnipeg Regional Health Authority, the entity that oversees all of the nursing homes in Winnipeg, would assign a case coordinator to complete an application for long-term care on my mother's behalf. Next, the case coordinator would present the application to the Long Term Care Access Centre Panel Review Board, which would determine the most appropriate care option for my mother. If the Panel Review Board approved my mother's placement in a nursing home, her name would be assigned to a waiting list for our preferred and alternate choice facility. Sande hoped the case coordinator could persuade the Panel Review Board that my mother's case should be designated community urgent, which meant that she would be awarded priority standing, but we would have to choose a facility from a list of four. All we could do was start the process and hope for the best.

The first hurdle would be to convince my mother to meet her case coordinator. Sande graciously agreed to facilitate the visit but my mother seemed to instinctively sense danger and refused to schedule an appointment.

*I'm too busy to see you. Don't bother coming by. I've got things on the go today. I don't have time for you.*

Finally, Sande elected a more direct approach. With the case coordinator in tow, she arrived on my mother's doorstep without advance notice. Peering through the glass triangles in her front door, my mother initially refused Sande and her companion entrance. She relented and allowed them into the house only when it became apparent that Sande was not prepared to admit defeat easily.

"I can't talk. I'm getting ready to move to Ontario," she told them.

Fortunately, the case coordinator had reviewed Sande's file and had most of the information she required. My mother's behaviour confirmed everything she had read. A short conversation – which was all my mother would spare the time for in any event – was what she needed to make her report.

"There's no question," she told Sande. "Mrs. Murray requires immediate placement in a personal care home."

With the case coordinator on side, Jeff and I were optimistic that my mother would receive community urgent status when the Panel Review Board assessed her application on the eighth of October. We had already toured several nursing homes and we were pleased to learn that our first choice, West Park Manor, would be on the list of possibilities for community urgent placement. The Director of West Park Manor, Reuben LaTour, was sympathetic to our situation and had agreed to give my mother priority on his waiting list as soon as her application was approved. The only stumbling block was that West Park Manor had to conduct its own admission interview before it would accept my mother as a potential resident. We had no idea how we could make that happen.

Reuben LaTour came to our rescue. It wasn't his job to conduct admission interviews, especially an undercover admission interview at a potential resident's home. Nevertheless, that's exactly what he agreed to do for us. Jeff was teaching a course in the Faculty of Law at the University of Manitoba on Friday mornings. In past years, he had often stopped in to see my mother on his way back to the office. This year it was part of his regular routine. A visit from Jeff on a Friday afternoon would not be an unusual event for my mother, and so it was arranged that Reuben would accompany Jeff on one of those visits. He agreed that neither his affiliation with West Park Manor nor his purpose would be mentioned.

Reuben parked in front of my mother's house just as Jeff drove into the driveway. Given my mother's now common practice of scouring the street for suspicious vehicles or people monitoring her movement, their timing couldn't have been better.

With Reuben at his side, Jeff rang the doorbell. A minute passed without any sound or activity inside the house. Jeff, already concerned about my mother's reaction to their presence, became worried that the meeting wasn't going to happen at all. He rang the bell again, and followed up with a firm knock. There was still no sign of life on the other side of the door. He turned to look at Reuben just as my mother emerged from her neighbour's house across the street. He relaxed, but only a little.

"I thought that was you, Jeff," my mother said when she joined the men on her front step. "I was watching the house from the Zwarichs'. That hobo was looking through my door again this morning. I wanted to see if he came back so I could point him out to Muriel."

Reuben looked at Jeff. Jeff shook his head. "So how do you know Jeff?" my mother asked as the three of them settled into chairs around the kitchen table. "Were you schoolmates?"

She eyed him over the top of her glasses.

"No, we're recent friends," Reuben replied, and deftly changed the subject to the length of time that my mother had been living in her house and whether she found it lonely living alone.

That was all the encouragement my mother needed to complain that everything was fine until Dr. Kalansky and I decided she had *debenture* and took away her driver's license. She filled the next thirty minutes with her usual stories about my misdeeds, as well as her more recent concern that the government intended to confiscate her property. Jeff called an end to the visit when he thought Reuben had had enough.

"Come back anytime," my mother told Reuben as he and Jeff were leaving.

SINCE SHE HAD been declared incompetent, my mother had become increasingly anxious. She was either not sleeping at all or sleeping during the day and staying awake all night. When she remembered, which was all too frequently, she obsessed about *the government* taking her property, and that she was going to be *thrown into a home for the aged*. We walked a fine line between not lying to my mother, and not telling her the whole truth, which we felt would only exacerbate her anxiety.

My mother was constantly conceiving schemes, some more outlandish than others, to thwart the government's effort.

*I'll give you everything I own, and then there won't be anything for the government to take.*

*I'll transfer the house into your name and then you and Jeff and Davis can move in here with me.*

*I'm leaving everything and moving to Ontario.*

Although she hadn't done anything concrete to realize any of her plans, we were constantly on guard. As a result, we chose not to tell my mother that she would be moving into a nursing home in the near future.

Liz and Jeff really conned me this time. I was busy cleaning the garage up and just put the car outside the door, then Jeff asked if we could all go for a drive around, we did and when we got back he stayed in the car and drove off. I figured they were going to get Liz's car and bring mine back, instead he took off with it. I waited for some time then decided to call them, see if they had gone home. I don't know how they got home so fast. I didn't intend for him to take my car home with different things of mine in it however when I contacted them to see where the car was they said it was at their house. How deceitful they both were and so friendly when we were together, they put one over on me. Jeff said they were keeping the car as I'm not supposed to be driving etc. He is as crooked as she is.

CALL POLICE — ASK IF THEY CAN CHECK IT OUT FOR ME SINCE AS FAR AS I'M CONCERNED IT'S A STOLEN CAR

Yesterday I took my car out of the garage and just parked it in front of the garage door - left the keys in it. Elizabeth and Jeff Hirsch came along in her van - and noticed the keys were in my car - Jeff came in and told me they were taking the car as I wasn't supposed to be driving - Liz had told me some time ago I had Alzheimers disease - Dr. Kalansky had said (I can explain that later)

They live in Wpg. He is a lawyer. They have a cottage at Victoria Beach and the way they were talking I think they were going to take my car there and leave it - I still own it and intend to drive it again

What I want is for you to advise me - its their idea to take the car to their cottage and leave it there - isn't that stealing my car?

Could you please tell them to bring my car back etc. this was all made up by Elizabeth

a very domineering woman came up to the
door about 2 days ago she was supposedly
working with Dr. Dyck but she didn't seem
like a nurse to me - claimed she was at that
hospital when I went in the spring re my leg -
at that time they sent a young man in a large car
with 3 seats in it to get me

woman wasn't even interested in my leg - came
up with the threat that Liz would have me put
away for good

want no part of Liz anymore - going to sell up
and go back to Ontario - where I came from

THREATENED to have me put away for good over
ownership unless Liz gets house and cottage etc.

said not mental capable

Letter said not of sound mind will have me
put away for good - have had threats - not
capable of looking after myself -

Sell and go back to Ontario - where I came from

FRIENDS IN ONT. WHO MIGHT HELP ME OUT
HELEN WOOD - ✔
PETER KURITA - ✔
ETHEL HIGGINSON - ✔
GOLDIE & JIGGS - ✔
ONA REYCRAFT        DIED MAY/07

PETER KURITA
1-905-366-0261
NO ANSWER 2:30 PM

CAROL
1-905-394-8471
NO ANSWER LEFT WORD 3:20
NO ANSWER 4:05

MARION FLEMING
1-416-943-4466
3:05 TOLD HER WHAT WAS HAPPENING

NEIL & BARB
350 QUEENSTON
NO ANSWER

GOLDIE
1-905-494-8573
NO ANSWER

<u>This is to be read out before Will (if I have one) after I die</u>

Liz is putting me in a home for the aged even though I take care of myself - cut lawns in summer - clean house twice a week - read more than watch T.V. - sew a lot - go for long walks often to shopping centre or bank

Liz is still holding it against me for not letting her & Jeff have the cottage and never going down again. Now she wants everything.

made darn sure I never can have a drivers license again - Kalansky who despises me is right in with her

Winnipeg Free Press
237 McDermot Ave, Winnipeg

Ms. L. Renolds:

Have been reading your columns for many years, and wondered if you would be interested in my story, as it may deter others from getting into the position I have been put in.

Hoping to hear from you.

Mamie Murray
42 Thatcher Drive, 269-7427

# Chapter Seventeen

**"I THINK SHE** means it this time."

According to my cousin Carol, my mother had moved beyond the talking stage and was preparing to put her escape plan into action. I couldn't help but marvel that my eighty-six-year-old mother's independent, feisty spirit was still intact. My mother had never played by the rules and it was clear that she wasn't about to start.

She had informed Carol of three different arrival dates and times but her strategy stayed the same. She would stay with Carol in Hamilton until the government stopped looking for her, at which time she would move to Campbellford and build a house in the same design as the one she had left in Winnipeg. My cousin had sounded a little desperate at the thought of my mother landing on her doorstep for an undetermined period of time, and while it did occur to me that my mother's departure would give me a much needed break, I knew I couldn't let it happen.

I called WestJet and hoped that I would be connected to a sympathetic customer service agent, preferably one who had an elderly parent with dementia. The woman who answered the telephone listened as I told her my problem.

"Passenger lists are confidential," she said. "But tell me the flights your mother may have booked and I'll see what I can do for you."

I offered the woman my mother's name along with the date, flight number, and potential arrival time. There was the distinctive tap-tap-tap of typing on a keyboard and then all I could hear was the sound of the woman breathing.

"Ellen May Murray isn't listed on the passenger list for that flight," she said finally. She sounded as relieved as I felt.

I gave the agent details of the second option. My mother wasn't listed on that flight either. Maybe Carol had overreacted, I thought, as I recited the itinerary of the last possibility and waited for the woman's response.

"That's all the information I can give you," she said after a pause that was longer than the previous two. "I hope you understand."

I had lulled myself into a false belief that the woman was prepared to breach whatever protocol existed and answer all of my questions. I took a deep breath and thought about what she had told me.

"Here's a hypothetical," I replied. "If my mother had purchased a ticket on one of the flights we've talked about, how would I go about cancelling it? She's currently a ward of the Public Trustee."

The woman put me on hold while she consulted someone higher in the chain of command. "We've never encountered a situation like this," she said when she returned. "We'll need to talk with someone in authority from the Public Trustee's office."

```
From:      "evmurray"
To:        "Kevin Murray"
Sent:      October 10, 2007 9:18 AM
Subject:   Update
```

Kevin,
Carol Winstanley called me yesterday and told me that Mom had booked a flight to Hamilton. Mom's plan was to hide out with Carol to prevent the government from "throwing her into a home for the aged."
With the help of Marla Winnings, the person at the Public Trustee's office who is overseeing Mom's file, we managed to cancel the plane reservation. When Marla called Mom and told her the flight was cancelled, Mom said she had to get to Hamilton for a funeral and mentioned trains and buses. Marla told Mom that she wasn't allowed to leave Winnipeg at all right now.
I'm sure Mom didn't understand who Marla was but when I was with Mom yesterday afternoon she did say that "the government wouldn't let her go anywhere." I told her she couldn't leave Winnipeg because she was under the care of the Public Trustee and that the police would bring her back to Winnipeg if she did leave. Mom asked if they would "stop her at the airport" and I said that they probably would. I added the bus station and train station for good measure.
I managed to take Mom's Visa card yesterday so hopefully this won't happen again. I also had Marla contact the CIBC to prevent Mom from withdrawing more than $100.
In the meantime, as I told you, we're No. 1 priority at West Park Manor. We've already done the pre-admission

```
interview — clandestinely — so we're ready to go when a
space becomes available.
Liz
```

My mother accepted her failed escape with surprising equanimity. She was pleased that she had what she considered real evidence to confirm the suspicion that she had been voicing over the past month.

"How would that woman have known I was going to Hamilton if she wasn't recording my telephone calls?" my mother asked.

It didn't occur to her that Carol and I had been involved in the transmission of information and she seemed prepared to finger the government as the guilty party. It wasn't long before my mother slyly decided that her sensitive communication should be conducted by regular mail rather than over the telephone. She removed the thick elastic band that held together her address book and sorted through the pages.

"I think Peter Kurita is my best bet," she said. "I did him a favour during the war and he's never forgotten. And besides," she continued, "he's already told me he would help me move to Ontario. He and Miriam have been looking for a house for me. They think it's terrible what's gone on here over the last few years."

She glared at me to enforce that she considered me responsible.

My mother's plan was for Peter Kurita to drive her to Campbellford and avoid the problem of police at the airport. I had visions of an RCMP blockade at the Manitoba-Ontario border and my mother lying under a blanket in the back seat of a car. It wouldn't happen, but the fact that she was still contemplating escape routes made me nervous.

MY MOTHER WAS still inclined to share her theory with others about my role in her downfall but she had been less hostile towards me in recent weeks. She hadn't refused me entry to her house. She regularly allowed me to take her grocery shopping. Her friendlier attitude was motivated by her need for a strategic alliance rather than a desire for reconciliation, a by-product of her decision to avoid fighting a battle on two fronts. For now, the government was my mother's primary enemy, which meant that a truce with me, even a reluctant truce, was in her best interest.

For the longest time, Jeff had been the only person I could talk to about my mother's behaviour. I was ashamed that she had turned against me. Even though I knew intellectually that her illness was responsible for her anger, it was harder to convince myself emotionally. I tortured myself with questions about what had I done to make my mother hate me.

Most of my friends knew that my mother had lost her driver's license. A few more knew that she was suffering from dementia. Until the spring of 2007, only one or two knew about the deterioration of our relationship. It was difficult to convince myself that others wouldn't believe that I had provoked my mother's ill will so I parsed out information cautiously.

When I finally allowed myself to talk more openly about how my mother was treating me, I realized how isolated I had let myself become. Sharing the information gave me a huge sense of relief. I was amazed how much emotional energy I had been spending trying to pretend that everything was all right – that even though my mother had dementia, my relationship with her hadn't changed.

Most of my friends had guessed something was wrong before I told them.

"Your mom was always around and then suddenly she wasn't," one said.

"Your mom stopped coming to Davis' hockey games. That just wasn't like her," another told me.

No one suggested that I was at fault. Every one offered unconditional support. It made me wish that I had been braver sooner.

I knew that I had to call Father Henry to talk about my mother's illness but I had avoided the conversation for as long as possible. Confessing to my friends was one thing; confessing to a minister who was my mother's confidant was another.

"Oh, Elizabeth, I'm so glad you called," Father Henry said. "I've been wanting to talk to you."

The next afternoon, he sat on the edge of the couch in my living room as I described my mother's behaviour over the last couple of years. He leaned forward, resting his elbows on his knees and clasping his hands in front of him as if in prayer. His gaze was sorrowful by the time I had explained the involvement of the Public Trustee, my mother's imminent move to a nursing home and her desperate attempts to escape.

"I should have called you sooner," he said gently, shaking his head slowly from side to side. "Do you remember when you came to Mamie's and I was visiting? It was about two years ago. She told me that you had been spying on her. The way she was talking about you – I knew that something was wrong with her. You've always been her eyeball."

I took a quivery breath and smiled at Father Henry's expression, which I understood to be the Jamaican version of "the apple of her eye".

"I feel terrible," I told him, again wishing I had been brave enough to share my concerns about my mother sooner. "I know she's going to be so unhappy in a nursing home."

"Don't feel terrible, Elizabeth. You've done your very best."

Father Henry's words echoed in my mind long after he had gone. I hoped that he was right.

A couple of days later, my mother accepted my invitation to come for dinner. She hadn't been to our house since October 2005 when she had first accused me of sabotaging her efforts to regain her driver's license. Jeff and I were both a little nervous about the evening but my mother arrived on her best behaviour. Our dinner conversation revolved around Davis' activities and accomplishments – topics that had always been of interest to her. She ate a generous amount of baked salmon and rice, followed by a big piece of chocolate cake. She repeatedly told me how wonderful everything tasted.

After dinner the four of us moved into the family room. My mother sat at one end of the couch. Davis dropped onto the seat beside her. He was too big to sit on her knee but he still wanted to be close. Jeff was in charge of the remote control and flipped between a news program and an NHL hockey game. My mother, whose only television was an eighteen-inch Sony she won in a draw at Shopper's Drug Mart in the early 1990s, marvelled at the technology of our big screen. Davis had been uncharacteristically quiet throughout the evening. He understood the nature of my mother's illness but he had difficulty dealing with the dichotomy between her largely unchanged physical appearance and her deteriorated mental condition.

An hour or so later Jeff gave me our private signal that it was time to bring the evening to a close.

"Well Mother-in-law," he said, after I gave him a nod of acknowledgment, "I think it's about time I drove you home."

We had previously agreed that it would be safer for him to do the honours at the end of our visit.

My mother pushed herself to her feet and then abruptly sank back down. She covered her face with both hands and her shoulders shook as she began to cry.

"I've been such a fool. I've missed being here so much."

Jeff and I were both surprised at my mother's rare show of insight. In the earlier stages of her dementia her lucidity would have made me question whether she really had the disease. Now it just made me sad. I was sadder still as Davis put his arm around his grandmother and looked at me with eyes that were full of anguish.

My mother wasn't the only one who cried that night.


WHEN I BEGAN the process to have my mother found incompetent and moved into a nursing home, I never imagined that it would be so fraught with complications. From the time Daryl Dyck arranged for my mother's informal competency assessment at Riverview Day Hospital, nothing had been easy or straightforward. Missed appointments, clandestine home visits, surreptitious evaluations, and desperate escape plans – we had devised, contrived or thwarted them all. We were like the scientists who studied the activity of Mount Vesuvius, constantly watching for signs that would prophesize potential catastrophe.

Despite our vigilance we were oblivious to the latent disaster that should have been apparent to anyone who was aware of our ultimate goal. We hadn't considered the crucial step of how we were going to get my mother to the nursing home, even though we had known that she would never go voluntarily.

Sande Kliewer and Dr. Blakely were adamant that I should not be the one to deliver my mother to her new residence. Since I was her primary caregiver, they said, it would be better if I didn't have to shoulder all of the blame or responsibility for the move. Sande had developed a good relationship with my mother and would have been able to persuade her to go for a car ride but that was outside the parameters of Sande's employment contract. She suggested that we could enlist the help of the Vulnerable Persons Unit of the Winnipeg Police Service, but they told me they didn't have the authority to remove my mother from her home at my request even if I was my mother's committee. The Public Trustee's office, while sympathetic, couldn't provide a solution to our problem either.

The court date for my application to replace the Public Trustee as my mother's committee was quickly approaching. As long as the Public Trustee was in charge, getting my mother to the nursing home was legally their responsibility. Until we had resolved the transportation issue we wanted to have the authority of the Public Trustee behind us. Jeff and I decided that my application ought to be adjourned.

I emailed Kevin and Neil to see what assistance they were prepared to offer. Neil telephoned me as soon as he received my message. He was sympathetic but couldn't provide a useful strategy.

Kevin's response was more detailed.

"This can't be the first time this has come up?!" his email began. He thought we were avoiding the inevitable and ought to tell my mother that she was moving to a nursing home. He stated that it would be difficult for him to come to Winnipeg on short notice but that he might be able to work something out if necessary.

I was frustrated by what I perceived to be Kevin's failure to recognize and appreciate everything that Jeff and I were doing. I wondered what would happen if I said that I couldn't cope anymore – that I wasn't sleeping properly and I jumped every time the telephone rang because I was afraid it meant something terrible had befallen my mother. Or if I said that Jeff had important work to do too and could no longer spend his days devising a solution for each new problem we faced.

```
From:      "evmurray"
To:        "Kevin Murray"
Sent:      October 18, 2007 4:46 PM
Subject:   Re: Mom Update
```

Actually Sande Kliewer and Marla Winning at the Public Trustee's office both assure us that our situation is "very unique."
However, Jeff did find a section in The Mental Health Act that he believes the Public Trustee can use to intervene and transport Mom to a "place of safety." He has discussed this tactic with Marla Winning, and she is willing to cooperate if Sande Kliewer can confirm that Mom's mental health is deteriorating. (Sande has no problem providing that confirmation.) We seem to be on track for the Public Trustee to direct the police — likely a Vulnerable Persons Officer — to take Mom to West Park when a bed becomes available. In order for this to work the Public Trustee must remain committee until the move occurs.
I don't think it's a good idea to tell Mom she's moving to a nursing home, at least at this point. First, it will cause her additional anxiety, which she doesn't need. Second, it will immediately make it more difficult for me to monitor her situation. Third, Mom is already a flight risk and disclosing that she is going to a nursing home would exacerbate the problem.
You are aware of Mom's attempt to fly to Hamilton last Wednesday. On Saturday morning, Carol Winstanley called and said that Mom had left a message at 2:30 AM indicating

that she had booked another flight. I called WestJet and
was told that Mom had reserved, but not paid for, a flight
leaving Sunday morning. Since I now have Mom's Visa card
I thought we were probably safe, but to be sure, Jeff and
I spoke to the police officers stationed at the airport.
Jeff faxed them proof that Mom is under the care of the
Public Trustee, and they agreed to put her name on a "no
fly" list with WestJet and Air Canada. At 4:40 this morning
we received a call from Duffy's Taxi (Sande Kliewer has
arranged for Duffy's to contact us whenever they receive a
call from Mom) indicating that Mom wanted to be picked up
at 6:00 and driven to the airport. We were going to cancel
the request but decided that this was an opportunity to
get her out of the house without intervention by the
police. We alerted the airport police, and arranged for
them to transport Mom to the Victoria Hospital. However,
when the taxi arrived, Mom told the driver she had changed
her mind.
This is just one example of what Jeff and I are dealing
with. Mom is definitely deteriorating with the stress of
waiting for placement.
Thank you for offering to come in if necessary. Hopefully
it won't be required.
Liz

I HAD DEVELOPED a love-hate relationship with the obituary section of
the *Winnipeg Free Press* shortly after I had been diagnosed with cancer. For
several years, I turned to the death announcements as soon as I unfolded the
newspaper and anxiously perused the columns to see if cancer had claimed
the life of any women in my age bracket. I mentally catalogued the details
of each death I discovered according to type of cancer, length of time the
deceased had been ill or had the disease, and the number and approximate
ages of surviving relatives. My obsession reminded me how lucky I was to be
alive but it also reinforced my fear that my luck could change at any moment.
I grew to hate the suggestion that the deceased had "fought courageously."
What other choice, I thought, did the poor woman have?

The obituaries had not been my first destination in the morning paper
for some time but the grim reality was that in order for there to be a vacancy
at a nursing home, someone had to die. Now I focused on the pictures and

birthdates of older people, looking for the likeliest former nursing home residents. A quick scan of the first paragraph, which usually revealed the place of death, and the last paragraph, where medical professionals and nursing home attendants were typically acknowledged, told me everything I needed to know. My diligence was rewarded on October 30. An elderly man had passed away at West Park Manor two days earlier. I immediately picked up the telephone and called Reuben LaTour.

"The man who passed away lived on the Alzheimer's ward," he said, referencing the locked unit reserved for patients in advanced stages of the disease. "Your mother doesn't need to be there yet so I'm waiting to see how we're going to shift people around."

He went on to tell me that he was trying to arrange for a private room for my mother. Residents were generally required to move into a double room first and wait their turn for a single to become available but Reuben understood that my mother was not a typical nursing home patient. Although she had dementia she was still remarkably independent and was more able physically than most people her age. The transition to West Park Manor was going to be difficult enough for her without having to cope with a roommate.

"I'll let you know what's going on as soon as possible," he assured me.

```
From:      "evmurray"
To:        "Kevin Murray; Neil Murray"
Sent:      October 31, 2007  5:03 PM
Subject:   Mom
```

A place is now available at West Park Manor. The scheduled move date is Tuesday, Nov. 6. We are still working out the details with the Public Trustee as to how that will take place. The likely scenario is that Sande Kliewer will be present at Mom's house but police officers from the Vulnerable Persons Unit will actually transport Mom to West Park. I will be waiting at the nursing home to assist her with the intake process. A condition of her being accepted at West Park Manor (given her reluctance to leave her home and her flight risk) is that we hire a companion to be with Mom four hours a day until she is settled. I have made that arrangement. I anticipate the next couple of weeks will be very difficult but hopefully things will

slowly start to improve thereafter. Mom is sleeping during
the day a lot more now and has said on several occasions
lately that she is bored at home.
Liz


By eleven o'clock on Tuesday, November 6, Jeff and I had been sitting in
an office on the second floor of West Park Manor for over an hour and a half.
We had met Brenda Warren, the head nurse on the ward where my mother's
private room would be located. We had completed all of the necessary paper
work and exhausted all small talk. Brenda had short grey hair that looked as
if it had been pressed, strand by strand. She wasn't eager to have an unwilling,
potential flight risk under her charge.

I checked my watch for the fifth time in as many minutes. Sande Kliewer
had arranged to meet two police officers from the Vulnerable Persons Unit
at my mother's house at nine o'clock. She was to remain outside while the
officers advised my mother that the Public Trustee had ordered them to take
her to West Park Manor. I was afraid that my mother would be permanently
scarred from the experience.

When we arrived, a handful of residents were congregated around the
large screen television in the main floor sitting room. They all seemed so
much older and feebler than my mother. As we continued down the corridor,
the smell of an ammonia-based disinfectant in the halls left an unpleasant
taste in my throat. I saw an old woman standing in the doorway of her room,
hunched over a walker, struggling to catch her breath. She stretched out her
arm and moved her lips in a silent plea for help.

Maybe my mother didn't belong here after all. Maybe she should be
coming to live with me as I had always imagined she would when she could
no longer manage on her own.

I thought about the spacious bedroom that my mother was leaving
behind. Windows that ran the full length of the room provided the perfect
vantage point for surveying the cars driving down the front street. There was
a time when I didn't want my mother to leave the house without me; even a

trip to the grocery store was an adventure I didn't want to miss. When my mother did venture out on her own I would stand in front of her bedroom window on my tiptoes and watch the activity on the street below, promising myself that the next car, or the one after that would be my mother's 1965 Dodge. In the weeks and months ahead no matter how many cars passed by that window, none of them would be bringing my mother home.

A sharp knock startled me. Sande Kliewer pushed open the door to the Head Nurse's office. She looked tired and drawn, as if she had just run a half marathon.

"Your mother's downstairs," Sande said. "I've been sitting with her for the last forty-five minutes. She's finally stopped crying."

Sande paused and rubbed her forehead. Her eyes were moist.

"What a morning."

She told us that she had met the police officers outside my mother's house as planned. The officers were armed with a letter from the Public Trustee's office that clearly outlined their mission. They knew what they had to do. After spending ten minutes with my mother inside the house they were back at Sande's side without their cargo.

"She says there's nothing wrong with her," they told Sande. "She says she's perfectly capable of living on her own. There must be some mistake."

I wasn't entirely surprised to hear Sande's story. People who met my mother casually, who just exchanged superficial small talk and didn't have an opportunity to engage her in conversation, might never have guessed her problem. If my mother experienced a memory lapse, or said something that didn't quite make sense, a person could easily dismiss it as a something that normally occurred with increased age. Even if she started talking about how *nasty* or *spiteful* I was, people who didn't know me might be justified in thinking the worst. The fact that my mother looked so good for her age helped her maintain an illusion of normalcy.

"I convinced the officers to go back inside with me," Sande continued. "I knew the right questions to ask to get your mother going. It didn't take long."

Brenda Warren's lips formed an upside-down crescent moon.

"Maybe this isn't the place for Mrs. Murray," she said.

Sande's eyes turned from water to ice. Her voice became sharp and each sentence landed with the firm thud of a knife hitting a chopping board.

"Mrs. Murray's dementia doesn't conform to the standard models. But she still has dementia. So where else can she go? It isn't safe for her to live on her own anymore."

My mother had accused me of being a bad daughter many times during the last two years, and that morning I had feared she was right. As Sande defended our decision, I felt a rush of relief. Perhaps my mother didn't belong in West Park Manor. Unfortunately, there was no alternative.

```
From:     "evmurray"
To:       "Kevin Murray"
Sent:     November 6, 2007    8:26 PM
Subject:  Mom
```

Just a follow up to my telephone message this afternoon that confirmed Mom's move to West Park Manor was successful. Reuben LaTour said she was very upset when she first arrived but after a while she calmed down and participated in some activities. Jeff and I were at the nursing home in an upstairs office but at about 3:30, Reuben suggested that it would be better if I didn't visit Mom today. He said that the staff thought Mom was settling in quite well but thought she might become anxious if she saw me. I would have preferred to check on Mom myself, but obviously I followed his advice.

As soon as it is recommended, I will have a phone line installed in Mom's room so you can call her. I think I told you earlier that she has a private room. Usually newcomers are put in a semi-private, but given Mom's unique circumstances they allowed her to have a private. I'll let you know how things are tomorrow.
Liz

```
From:     "evmurray"
To:       "Kevin Murray"
Sent:     November 7, 2007    7:04 PM
Subject:  Mom
```

The reports from the home are all good. Mom is participating in activities and seems to be adapting better than expected.

```
The staff feels it is best if she doesn't have outside
contact for a few more days as things are progressing
well. I am uncomfortable with this as I would like to see
her but I am following their advice.
Liz
```

My mother had been in West Park Manor for two days and I hadn't seen her since the evening before she was taken from her home. As I entered the front door of the nursing home I felt like I was meeting a childhood friend whose life had taken a different path and all we had in common was the past. The same residents were crowded around the television in the main floor sitting room and the facility still smelled of disinfectant. I tried not to look around as I hurried to the elevator that would take me to my mother. If I found the atmosphere overwhelming, I could only imagine how she was feeling.

An open area on the upper level overlooked the main floor. My mother and a matronly woman stood side by side watching the activity below them. They would have been able to monitor my arrival from their vantage point but if my mother was aware that I was coming she was studiously avoiding any sign of welcome.

"Hey, Mom," I touched her shoulder from behind.

When she turned to look at me her tight lips told me that I had been expected. Her arms remained by her side as I gave her a gentle hug.

"What are you doing here?" she demanded. "I –"

She stopped abruptly and glanced sideways to see if her companion was paying attention to our exchange, and then quickly adjusted her expression from anger to something approximating delight. My mother hooked her right arm through the other woman's left elbow.

"This is my friend –" her voice petered out.

"Beryl," the woman interjected.

"Beryl," my mother repeated. "We ran into each other the first day I was here and we've been good friends ever since."

```
From:     "evmurray"
To:       "Kevin Murray"
Sent:     November 8, 2007 7:10 PM
Subject: Mom
```

I finally saw Mom today. She was doing okay but asked, "Why am I here?" and "How long am I going to be here?" She would like to talk to you. I will find out tomorrow how that can work since she doesn't have her own phone yet. She really likes her new companion, Beryl.
Liz

The days that followed were difficult. The staff at West Park Manor told my mother repeatedly that it was the Public Trustee who decided that she ought to be living in the nursing home but my mother soon developed her own theories about who was to blame. Her most common complaint became *that Dr. Blakely*, or that woman who came to see her in the summer who claimed to be a doctor. She said that *Dr. Blakely had boasted that she would get even.*

Brenda Warren, who had proved to be my staunch ally, said that my mother also accused me of engineering her confinement. That indictment was reserved for ears other than my own. When I was with my mother, she focused less on what she suspected I had done to her in the past and more on what I was failing to do for her in the present.

*You could get me out of here if you really wanted to.*

*I would never have left my mother in a place like this.*

*What kind of daughter are you?*

When I told her that I didn't have the authority to decide where she was to live, she asked me what I was good for. Kevin, she advised me repeatedly, would come and *straighten things out.*

I was often crying as I walked from my mother's room, past the nursing station to the elevator. Several times Brenda suggested that it would be okay for me to take a few days off from visiting my mother, but I felt guilty if I didn't stop by every day for at least a short time. I told myself that I should be strong enough to set my hurt feelings aside and empathize with my mother. Her world was disintegrating around her and she was reacting in the only way she could.

I kept Kevin informed with regular messages about how my mother was adapting to her situation and the problems I was encountering. I was pleased when he disclosed that he was arranging an overnight trip to Winnipeg to assess her progress himself.

"Please let me know the specifics of your visit when you have made your plans," I requested. I had hoped that we could meet and agree upon the best approach to deal with my mother's ongoing questions and concerns.

On November eighteenth, I received an email from Kevin saying that he had been to Winnipeg to see my mother. He described his visit as profoundly depressing.

```
From:      "evmurray"
To:        "Kevin Murray"
Sent:      November 20, 2007 9:53 AM
Subject:   Mom

Kevin,
I'm glad you were able to see Mom last Saturday. However,
I am disappointed you did not contact me in advance of
your visit as I had requested. There were a number of
issues I wanted to discuss with you, including how we
ought to approach telling Mom that there is nothing we can
do to get her out of care, as well as her long-term care
plan. I thought it would be in Mom's best interests if we
discussed the former with Mom together or at least agreed
upon a unified approach.
I am currently trying to organize Mom's financial matters
and slowly clean out the house. If there is anything in
the house you would like, please let me know.
Liz
```

TELL KEVIN

What I'm going to say is not to be mentioned to anyone not even Neil. His telephone is tapped but I guess he knows that as for quite a whiled now when I phone, he won't talk to me. I'm the slow one, guess mine has been tapped for quite some time. I feel angry that Liz is in his telephone.

Was going to Campbellford - called Peter Kurita and he was sending a car out for me, Liz knew all about it. Apparently she listened to all Peter and my conversations re going back to Ontario. Guess she really gave it to him. That's why I was stopped at both the train and flight stations and such a terrible thing made of it - they won't let me on a plane or train even - can you help me please or come down

Liz claims she owns my house and cottage although I've never turned them over to her. Do you think somehow you could get to the city to confirm all this - I'm already a nervous wreck but the house & cottage will be yours, I'm not trying to buy you off but maybe I could get a small apartment up where you are.

Please come up with a plan. I was going to get another car. Jeff took away my first one.

Liz has Odarka Trosky watching me, was going for a short walk the other day and Odarka was on her lawn, she came talking to me, was saying what a good daughter I had, really cares about me

Liz comes every afternoon to watch me. A while ago when I said I was going to get my license back she said I'd never pass the test.

Neil would you and Barb come over one nite soon, I think there is something important to discuss - but not on the phone - its about the phone line - as I think you know
Did you know Wanda Francey died

                              Mom

By the way we could put your car in the garage. Think you know what I know. Please reply by coming over and discussing this - don't say anything to Kevin (over the phone) about this. Your car can go in the garage?

---

Liz says I'm in here because I had new locks put on front door and wouldn't always let her in

Reason for new locks and not answering - worked in back yard (had to mow lawn)

was often in back sun porch reading - sometimes fell asleep on long chair

could have been in the back room watching T.V. - had certain programs I would watch

If I was working or checking things in basement (had wardrobe down there - would go down, change summer & winter clothes) as well as washing machine - also carpet on floor had to be vacuumed plus good chairs kept dusted plus sort of a day bed, cover was always kept clean

GO THROUGH HOUSE AND SEE, I WASN'T ALWAYS IN KITCHEN

IF I WAS always had sewing to do (have sewing machine) had to rehem pants dresses coats etc as I have shrunk in my old age - might not hear the door over the noise

Dear Peter and Miriam

This is my last piece of writing paper and only have one envelope, was hoping you would come out and see me and take me back to Ontario, nothing has changed here - Liz still means to throw me into a home for old people - she keeps coming to see me or mock me I don't know which, so if you come out I'm not going to say anything. I'm dying to get back to Ontario and hope you can help me, at least come and see me

Can't find any stamps in my drawer now although I found a couple yesterday and have sort of an idea where they went to. Please please come out. I would like to get back to Ontario.

Love Mamie

Dear Miriam and Peter:

Thank you so much for the nice letter and stamps.

Don't think I'm living in what you think, it's a one room and bathroom - no shower etc. just a sink. And no way to get to my Bank.

I wrote to you to see if Peter & you had any way of getting me out of this one room place and back to Ontario. Had a woman tell me last July or August she was going to put me in a home for the aged - about a week later I was brought to this one room place. No I'm not happy and would like to go to Ontario or my house that I own. Any help (lawyer etc) you could help me with, I'd greatly appreciate.

My own daughter is a very spiteful lawyer so no help at all. Think Elizabeth helped put me in here. Please come out so I can talk with you.

Mamie Murray

Dear Rev. Lanctot.

Thank you very much for the bulletin of December 2/2007. I should have written before but the bulletin has only just appeared in my room.

Father Henry could tell you how I was put in here etc. I would appreciate a visit from you as soon as it's possible so we can get to know each other.

I don't want to explain my position here, as I'd rather discuss it in person.

The flowers are beautiful, please give my thanks to the congregation.

What I need is a good lawyer so you may ask around and let me know. I was put in here suddenly, a matter of spite by my daughter.

Mamie Murray

# Chapter Eighteen

**MY FAMILY HOME** was full of forty-seven years of furniture, books, linens, clothes and assorted odds and ends that could no longer stay. In the months after my mother's move to the nursing home, I arrived armed with cardboard boxes, plastic garbage bags and good intentions, trying not to become distracted by memories of happier times. Whenever I was in the house I felt as if my mother was with me, looking over my shoulder to ensure that her belongings were being dealt with properly.

Initially I respected her imagined admonitions and sorted items into separate piles to keep, give away or discard. I was careful not to reject anything that might have had sentimental value for her but as my work dragged on I felt the weight of Sisyphus, condemned to forever roll a rock up a hill. Every drawer or closet I tackled was the same. I became less discriminating and eventually I was filling garbage bag after garbage bag with items that would just be thrown away.

The amount of clutter in the house seemed to have grown in proportion to my mother's cognitive decline. As a child of the Depression, she had always been a small-scale hoarder, but the randomness of the articles I found stockpiled was startling. The storage cupboard in the basement laundry room was filled with fifty or more pink boxes with cellophane windows in the lid, the kind that came from a grocery store bakery. Each had been wiped clean of crumbs and precisely stacked until they formed a cardboard pyramid. Two dozen or more round plastic trays with clear bubble tops that had once protected a cake or pie occupied another area. There were thirty boxes of cling wrap, even more of aluminum foil, and at least fifteen boxes of wax paper. Closer to the washing machine, I found twelve family-size jugs of liquid detergent and five large boxes of flakes.

The closet in the bedroom that my mother had considered Davis' was bursting with clothes. Half of the space was still dedicated to the wardrobe that she had maintained for her grandson when he was a little boy. The other half was crowded with blouses, skirts, and sweaters from a discount department store that had opened not far from my mother's house. Price tags still hung from many of the items that ranged in size from sixteen to twenty. Thirty years ago, when my mother was at her heaviest, she had occasionally worn a size fourteen. In recent years she was so diminished that I was sure that she wasn't larger than a size four. I wasn't surprised that the clothes had never been worn.

In the kitchen, two of my mother's favourite photographs were taped to the door of the refrigerator. The first was a picture of Davis and my father taken just a few weeks before my father had died. Four-month-old Davis was propped up in a chair; his round cheeks were shiny and red and almost completely obscured his eyes. My smiling father was kneeling beside the chair, one hand resting on his grandson's chubby knee. The second photo was of my mother and six other women at her seventy-fifth birthday party on May 7, 1996.

I had wanted to do something special to honour my mother's milestone birthday and so I offered to invite her friends for a ladies' lunch at my house. My mother was initially reluctant to agree to the plan, concerned that her friends might think the celebration was her idea rather than mine. For a few days it looked like the lunch wasn't going to happen.

My mother soon devised a scheme that involved a level of intrigue that I thought was both silly and unnecessary. The ladies would be invited to a surprise party and my mother would feign ignorance of the arrangements. I agreed to the ruse only because my mother wouldn't have it any other way.

Together we decided the guest list, selected invitations and planned the menu. On the day of the lunch I set the table with my Limoges Bird of Paradise china, a linen tablecloth and napkins and a bouquet of orange and yellow tulips. Six of her friends from church, all wearing skirts and coordinated cardigans or blazers, arrived at precisely fifteen minutes before noon. When my mother rang the doorbell half an hour later, they giggled like toddlers watching their favourite cartoons and scurried to position themselves so they wouldn't be visible when my mother first entered the house.

"Come on in, Mom," I said, trying to speak casually and avoid rolling my eyes. She was also dressed in a skirt and blazer; a silk scarf was tied into a jaunty bow at her neck.

"Okay, but I just have a minute," my mother replied, projecting her voice beyond the front foyer. "I've just come from the grocery store."

My mother and I rounded the corner into the family room.

"Surprise," the ladies chorused.

"Oh my," my mother shrieked, pretending to be startled. Her eyes were bright with anticipation.

Several hours later, my mother stood at the door and proudly accepted her friends' thanks. After we had waved our last good-bye, my mother looked at me and grinned.

"Thank you," she said. "That couldn't have been more perfect."

During my mother's last weeks in her house, she was convinced that she had heard scratching sounds in the night.

"I must have mice," she told me.

I was not convinced. My mother's claim seemed no different than her belief that there had been a hobo peering in her windows or a Royal Canadian Mounted Police officer climbing her basement stairs. I had called Jeff and asked him to purchase a mousetrap on his way home from work, only because it was easier than trying to convince my mother that she was wrong.

As I now emptied the kitchen cupboards of sugary cereals and cookies I discovered mouse droppings, unequivocal evidence that my mother's story was true. I was sickened by the thought that my mother had been living with mice and appalled that I had dismissed her complaints so cavalierly.

When Davis was in kindergarten, Jeff and I made a *Davis Calendar* for my mother for Christmas. In the middle of November we had Davis dress up in costumes appropriate for each month of the year and pose to have his picture taken. The gift was a huge success and for several years my mother pasted the

Davis pictures onto whatever calendar she had happened to receive in the mail. I found a 2006 calendar stuffed into the drawer beneath the stove with an assortment of pots and pans. I flipped through the pages, pausing from time to time to read my mother's notations. "Liz's Birthday" was printed in the square for June 19th. My eyes filled with tears.

Every time I slid open the front hall closet I saw the mink coat that my mother and I had purchased the winter after I had first been diagnosed with cancer. My mother wouldn't have a use for her china or silverware but I hoped that she might yet have an opportunity to wear her beloved fur. The coat reminded me of the love we shared and even if I never wore it, I could never give it away.

Pushed to the back of the top shelf in the linen closet was a large plastic bag filled with a treasury of report cards, projects and assignments that spanned the twelve years of my public school education. I selected a composition written in purple ink on pink lined paper that highlighted the dangers of smoking. On the last page, my Grade Five teacher had marked a large, red A-plus and noted that it was a well-organized and thoughtful report. My mother had always been proud of my good marks. She would tell me, half ruefully, that I was lucky that I got my father's brains.

When my mother talked about her childhood, she would say that her brother Peter was the smart one in the family. She regretted that she had no formal education beyond high school, and was impressed or even intimidated by women like Odarka Trosky who had university degrees. My mother had insisted on describing her friend, Eve Buhr, as a schoolteacher, as if teacher alone didn't carry enough weight or respect. For my mother, dementia had only been further proof that she didn't measure up intellectually.

Every room I tackled was littered with miscellaneous documents and detritus. Homogenized heaps mixed income tax returns, letters and bank statements with advertisements for long expired grocery specials, used envelopes and scraps of notepaper. Labels and logos from a variety of household products were layered with utility bills and ragged pages torn from *Chatelaine* or *The Ladies Home Journal*. Receipts verifying the payment of home insurance and property taxes were tucked into the folds of old newspapers. Pages that ought to be in sequence weren't; current documents were filed with those that were more than a decade old.

Each pile contained the notes in my mother's handwriting that I had come to expect and dread. Several notes referenced discussions or meetings with a lawyer, something that would have shocked me if Kevin hadn't advised me about the lawyer's letter he had found in my mother's file cabinet in September 2007.

The china cabinet where my doll collection had been proudly displayed for over thirty years now contained only an odd assortment of papers and debris. When I looked at its ragged contents, I felt angry with my mother. I knew that I should have directed that anger towards her disease but the destruction of my collection felt so personal that it wasn't easy to be rational.

The process of restoring order to my former bedroom was both soothing and disquieting. Sitting on the newly reclaimed floor by my bed, I was often reminded of happier times, when the room had been my sanctuary. The notes that Jeff had written to me just after we had met were still hidden inside the small wooden box that I had stashed in the bottom drawer of my dresser. Several sheets of foolscap showed the ridges where they had been folded in half once and then again and again to form the small packages that Jeff had passed me in the hallways of the law school at the University of Manitoba. The messages were fresh and innocent. *Meet me in the common room at noon. How about a movie tonight? I love you.*

I found the box for my wedding dress after I had culled through the wreckage deposited on my bed. My hand shook slightly as I opened the lid, the black letters describing its contents still clearly visible. The box was filled with threadbare towels, which ought to have been torn into dust rags or discarded. I closed the container and slowly walked out of the bedroom.

A small door in the wall of the second floor hallway accessed the crawlspace over the kitchen and living room. The opening wasn't large enough for me to pass through without my shoulders brushing the sides of the doorframe; the floor wasn't strong enough to hold my full weight unless I was crouching on one of the floor joists. I briefly considered ignoring the space and leaving its contents for the next homeowner to pore through but my mother had used it to store a variety of obsolete or broken items that she was convinced would *come in handy some day*. My curiosity prevailed. Manoeuvring awkwardly from joist to joist, I found a record player with a stack of warped LPs beside Kevin's Big Bruiser tow truck. My once cherished tin dollhouse peeked from behind a jumble of children's Halloween costumes. In the farthest corner of the crawlspace I spied a crushed cardboard box. Nothing on the outside of the twelve-inch cube revealed its contents.

I cautiously dragged the box to the daylight of the hallway. A sliver of white fabric was visible where the two top flaps didn't quite meet. When I wrenched the box open, my wedding dress sprang out like a Jack-in-the-box. For a moment, I marvelled at the tenacity it must have taken to jam the full-length dress into the carton.

The dress was badly creased but it wasn't ruined. As I lifted the material from its prison and shook out the folds, coloured paper fluttered to the ground like confetti. Some of the fragments fit together to form an image of me in cap and gown from my high school graduation; others became the stained glass window in the synagogue in which Jeff and I were married.

I discovered more pictures in a drawer in the dining room buffet, hidden among the tablecloths and napkins. The photograph of Jeff, Davis and me that had always been my mother's favourite was intact. My image had been ripped from two other pictures of my family, although in one, a remnant of my arm remained. In a picture of me alone, my face was covered in swirls of blue ink and holes had been poked where my eyes had once been.

One afternoon I wandered aimlessly from the living room to the dining room through the kitchen and around again. I had only an hour before I had to pick Davis up from school but I wasn't inspired by any of the jobs on my extensive to-do list. As I finished the second lap of my circuit my eyes were drawn to an old footstool that my parents had upholstered in the same gold shag carpeting that had once covered the floor of the recreation room and the family room. The stool had survived several leaks and minor floods over the years and smelled more than a little mouldy; my mother had inexplicably moved it from its usual spot in the basement to the farthest corner of the dining room where it was partially hidden by the table and two chairs.

The hollow space inside the footstool had once stored board games and puzzles. I assumed that it would now be a repository of still more papers but I felt anxious as I slowly opened the lid. Stuffed into the cavity of the footstool were four of the antique dolls that had been missing from the china cabinet when I conducted my rescue mission in December 2006. The legs of one were wrapped around the body of another; two bisque heads butted together, face to face. My most valuable doll, the one with the leather body and delicate lace dress, was lying on her back with her painted eyes staring up at me reproachfully. Without warning I was overtaken by huge, body-shaking sobs.

Some time later I found the rest of my missing dolls in a paper shopping bag that had been shoved to the back of the closet in the master bedroom. My mother's callous disregard for the condition of my dolls hurt me even more than her destruction of my pictures. The pictures were just pieces of paper; they didn't hold the same memories.

I never became immune to the evidence of my mother's malice. Every discovery was painful. Instead of developing a thicker skin, mine became blistered and sore. Eventually I began to personify my mother's disease. I told myself that my mother only acted on the instructions of dementia, that she had become the disease's unwilling amanuensis and servant. That rationalization helped most of the time but did little to reduce the sting of my next find.

Buried in a stack of debris in the family room was the letter from a lawyer dated November 16, 2005 that Kevin had described. The letter stated that it enclosed two copies of a Will that my mother had signed the week before.

Neither copy accompanied the letter but since she had made the Will soon after she had turned against me, I suspected the worst.

One copy of the document emerged a few days later in a separate heap of papers. My hand shook and the words faded in and out of focus as I scanned the text. My mother had disinherited me and had divided her estate equally between Neil, Kevin and Davis. It wasn't that my mother hadn't provided for me in her Will that upset me. What took my breath away was the rationale given for that decision. The words produced a persistent but indefinable ache in my heart, like the phantom pain from a missing limb.

The reasons for my disinheritance set out in the Will were simply those that would be easily recognized by any second or third year law student – justifications that had been established by the law. I knew that the lawyer had generated them, not my mother. I could imagine the questions that he would ask to elicit the answers he needed to follow her instructions.

*Do you have a close relationship with your daughter?*

*No, absolutely not. We've never had a close relationship.*

*Have you given your daughter substantial gifts that were intended to be advances on her future inheritance?*

*Yes, absolutely. I gave and gave to that girl and look what she's turned around and done to me.*

*Does your daughter have any special needs that cause her to require support from you?*

*No, there's nothing wrong with her except that she's mean and spiteful. She and her husband are both lawyers, after all.*

None of that knowledge eased my pain, nor did the notes she had made about her visit.

Days later, I found a second letter from the lawyer dated December 7, 2005. The lawyer stated that he was returning my mother's original Will in accordance with her telephone request and her indication that she intended to see a different lawyer to make some changes. The original Will was not with the letter; I didn't find it elsewhere in her house or in her safety deposit box. When a Will is last in the possession of the testator and cannot be found after death, the law presumes that the testator destroyed the Will with the intention of rendering it null and void.

Since my mother's Will was nowhere to be found, I chose to believe that she had had a change of heart and destroyed it. I told myself that my mother's love for me had triumphed over her illness; that ultimately she had destroyed the Will because she didn't want to do anything that would hurt me. I believed that those things were true, but the suggestion that my mother and I had never had a close relationship continued to haunt me.

Just as I had become accustomed to discovering unpleasant things in unexpected places in the house, I happened upon a special gift.

In 1979, my parents built a covered porch off the family room. The half-walls were cement; wooden posts connected screen panels and supported the corrugated plastic roof. It wasn't until the house was ready to sell that I realized the porch wasn't included on the copy of the surveyor's certificate that I had found with the property title. Further investigation confirmed that they hadn't obtained the required building permits when the porch was first constructed. Rather than delay the sale of the house while I applied for the appropriate documents, the simplest solution was to remove the structure.

Halfway through the demolition, a cardboard tube tumbled out of the wall closest to the house. The handyman brushed off clumps of dried cement and waved it in my direction. It was a time capsule containing a business section of the *Winnipeg Free Press*, an issue of *Macleans* magazine, a photocopy of the 1979 property tax bill for the house, and the program from my recent high school convocation. A note in my mother's handwriting stated my parents' names and the date.

I thought about the bright prospects that my mother had envisioned when she had tucked those pieces of history into the structure of our home. Despite our family's flaws, my childhood had been happy. I was loved and encouraged and I always knew that I had my mother's support. She would never have guessed the challenges that we would have to bear nor the upheaval we would face as we lived through her unravelling.

JOHN F. KENNEDY once said that the greatest enemy of truth is often not the lie – deliberate, contrived and dishonest – but the myth – persistent, persuasive and unrealistic. Dementia had been our relentless enemy, stalking my mother for months, blurring reality and convincing her of all the wrongs that she imagined I had committed.

# Chapter Nineteen

ON TUESDAY, JULY 29, 2008, just after five o'clock in the afternoon, a nurse from Seven Oaks Hospital where my mother had been staying since the end of June, called me at our cottage. "Your mother has a touch of pneumonia," she said calmly. "We've given her an antibiotic and we're monitoring her condition."

"Is she okay? Should I come?"

"It's not urgent at this point," the nurse replied.

"I'm at least an hour away from Winnipeg. Should I come?" I asked again.

"The antibiotic might help," she soothed. "I just wanted to let you know what was happening."

The nurse promised to keep me informed and I hung up the phone, not knowing what to do with myself. I opened the refrigerator thinking I should start chopping vegetables for a salad, but decided that I didn't have the patience for the job. I opened a cupboard and stared blankly at a box of whole wheat spaghetti, trying to force myself to think about what Davis might like to eat.

Instead, I picked up the phone and jabbed the numbers to connect me to Jeff at his law office. He knew that something was wrong as soon as he heard my voice – which was just about the same time I realized how frightened I was. I told him what the nurse had said and asked him if he would go to the hospital. Before I had finished talking he was shutting off his computer and putting on his suit jacket. He assured me that he would call as soon as he saw my mother, and I was left staring at the phone again. By now I was too nervous to just wait at the cottage for news. I started getting organized to drive into the city.

I scrambled to the car with Davis and a backpack containing a few clothes and toiletries that I thought I might need. Jeff called my cell phone just as we were turning onto the main highway.

"You should come," he said. "Don't rush. Your mom –"

"We're in the car," I interrupted, trying to keep the panic from my voice. "I'll be there soon." We both knew that it was pointless for him to tell me not to rush.

I didn't want to hear what Jeff was going to say about my mother's condition. I already knew that she was gravely ill – Jeff wouldn't have told me to come to the hospital otherwise. I pushed away a sinking feeling of fear and guilt, wishing I could turn back the clock to a time when my relationship with my mother had been easier.

Just seven weeks ago when my mother was first diagnosed with bowel cancer, I had to make the necessary decisions about her medical care. I knew that surgery was inevitable. The choice was whether to remove the tumour immediately, or wait until it caused an obstruction in her bowel. I worried that the general anaesthetic would accelerate her dementia and I hated the thought of causing my mother further confusion by initiating the surgery, but letting nature take its course didn't seem like a realistic option.

My mother had been in West Park Manor for almost eight months when she left for the hospital. Although she had occasionally agreed to participate in the scheduled activities at the nursing home, more often she paced the hallways by herself like a caged lioness. It was clear she had not been happy but while she was waiting at Seven Oaks for her surgery, she told me that she wanted to go back to *where she ate in the room at the end of the hallway.*

I knew it was just the strangeness of her situation that made my mother think fondly of the nursing home. And I knew it was the right decision for her to have surgery before her bowel became obstructed. I just couldn't help feeling that somehow my mother's unhappiness was entirely my fault. Kevin had told me that *I should follow her doctor's advice* and once I put aside the emotional aspect, there really wasn't much to consider. The tumour had to be removed, and since later would likely cause my mother more pain than sooner, sooner would be better.

After the operation, evidence of my mother's continued decline soon mounted. She could no longer walk without the assistance of a walker and even then her steps were slow and unsure. A catheter was removed, and then, despite my protests, replaced. For no physical reason that could be determined, my mother developed trouble swallowing which made eating a challenge. I hand-fed her tiny bits of her favourite salmon sandwiches. I offered her sips of milky rice puddings that I made from the recipe her own mother had followed. I crumbled pieces of the sticky buns that she had always craved, making sure there were no pecans that could stick in her throat – anything to persuade her to eat. As my eighty-seven-year-old mother became increasingly vulnerable, almost with each passing day, I felt my love for her even more acutely.

When Davis and I walked through the glass doors at the main entrance to the hospital, the air smelled stale and our footsteps echoed through the empty halls. The building seemed forlorn as we waited in silence for the elevator to take us to my mother's floor. The palms of my hands started to sweat. Everything was taking so much longer than I wanted it to.

The door to my mother's room was half-open. Jeff was sitting beside the hospital bed, reading out loud from a book that had been published to commemorate the one hundred and fiftieth anniversary of Campbellford. It had been Jeff's idea to bring the book to the hospital. He paused when he saw us in the doorway and tried to curve his mouth into a small smile; his eyes looked worried and sad.

My mother's bed was raised to a forty-five degree angle. Her hair, which she had always arranged in a flat curl to cover the lines on her forehead, was pushed back from her face. She looked like a snow angel, almost translucent against the stiff white bed sheets. Her eyes fluttered open. I wasn't sure if she could see us standing in the doorway, so I moved into the room and stood at the foot of her bed. Davis retreated to the hallway. I wasn't surprised that he found it difficult to see his grandmother when she was so ill.

I tried to continue reading to my mother after Jeff took Davis home. When I stumbled over the name of the veterinarian who had worked in

Campbellford for over fifty years, she corrected me in a hoarse whisper.

"John Trimble."

My voice wavered and I had to keep biting my lip so I wouldn't cry. Instead, I stroked the hand that had once lovingly caressed me, and listened to her raspy, uneasy breathing. A nurse rested her hand lightly on my mother's chest and adjusted an oxygen mask over her nose and mouth. She didn't need to tell me that my mother was becoming more congested.

My mother's mind had been battered and bruised for quite some time but her thin frame underneath the blue hospital blanket confirmed that her body and her spirit were now also depleted. Her struggle for air became more tortured. I squeezed her frail hand gingerly. At times it had been calloused and rough from the hard work she had never avoided. Now it was just skin over bone, as delicate as the skeleton of a sparrow. My mother had always been so vital, seemingly tireless in her desire to get things done. I had always said that she would live to be one hundred and twenty years old; that meant she shouldn't die for another thirty-three years. Even with all we had endured throughout her illness, I couldn't bear for her to die.

When I was pregnant, a friend gave me a copy of *Love You Forever* by Robert Munsch. The children's classic describes a mother who lovingly cares for her son as he grows from an infant to a man, and the son who cares for his mother just as lovingly when she becomes ill and feeble. The story made me weep – not for the relationship I hoped to have with my unborn child, but because it reflected so clearly the love and the sense of responsibility that I felt for my mother, and had felt for as long as I could remember. Alone together in her hospital room, I knew that I would miss my mother forever.

I glanced at my watch. Jeff had been gone forty-five minutes. I hoped he had been able to contact Father Henry as I had requested.

My mother's struggle to breathe intensified but she fought to remove the oxygen mask at every opportunity. Before my mother's bowel surgery, dementia had bolstered some aspects of her personality. She had become more single-minded, more paranoid, and more certain that her way was the only alternative. After surgery, she was timid, childlike, and uncertain. Her familiar edge was gone.

One day I had arrived on my mother's hospital ward to hear her repeatedly shouting, "Mamie Winstanley, 42 Thatcher Drive. Help me!" I was saddened by my mother's distress but heartened at her show of bravado. That incident was the exception – a lonely example of rebellion.

I held her oxygen mask in place and began to speak-sing a few bars of "You are my Sunshine." When I was a child, my mother used to take me on her knee, hug me tight, and sing those same verses. My voice was shaky and caught on most of the words but I was sure that her eyes brightened in acknowledgment.

A nurse entered the room and monitored my mother's laboured breathing.

"Can't you give her something to make her more comfortable?" I asked.

"She just had another dose of the antibiotic. We don't want to give her anything that will suppress her breathing until we know if it's going to work," the nurse replied softly.

Jeff and Father Henry arrived together about twenty minutes later. Time had passed slowly when I was alone but now suddenly quickened. Father Henry stood at the side of the bed and administered the last rites. He touched my mother's shoulder gently as he closed his prayer book and spoke the final words.

"May the Lord Jesus Christ protect you and lead you to eternal light."

I knew it was time to let her go but I wanted to shout *Not yet! I'm not ready yet!*

"I love you, Mom," I said, when I was finally able to speak.

She stopped struggling. Just before she lost consciousness she whispered her final goodbye.

"I love you too, Elizabeth."

# Epilogue

**MY MOTHER'S LAST** words comforted me in the immediate aftermath of her death. Despite how fractured our relationship had become, I was secure in the knowledge that my mother had always loved me.

My complacency didn't last. Psychological theories postulate that most people mourn the death of a loved one in stages that include denial, anger and depression. Dementia had claimed my mother long before her demise and I thought that I had already accepted my loss but when my anger arrived, it was intense.

Initially my rage was directed at my brothers. I was bitter that Kevin had ignored my entreaties for us to forget our differences and work together and I felt that Neil had sided with Kevin against me.

It wasn't long before my feelings were also directed at my mother. After so many years of being conscripted into service as her ally, after a lifetime of caring for and protecting her, how dare she turn against me? In the thick of her hatred I had learned to withstand her insults and move on to the next encounter. I rationalized and intellectualized her behaviour so that I could continue to fulfill the responsibility that had always been mine, but clearly I hadn't forgotten the pain she had inflicted. It became difficult for me to generate happy memories of my mother, and the notes she had left behind only fuelled my sense of injustice. My mother had twisted everything I had tried to do for her into something dark and evil.

Jeff's love and support sustained me through the difficult years with my mother. He was also there for me after her death, but in the same month that my mother languished in the hospital, his own mother was in palliative care in a different hospital at the opposite end of the city. Tonia died just five weeks after my mother, and Jeff was torn between my anguish and his own mourning. For almost twenty years my mother had tried to distance herself and me from Jeff's mother, but their deaths became inextricably linked. The irony wasn't lost on Jeff or me.

The original Will that my mother executed in November 2005 never did surface in the reams of paper that I cleaned out of her house. Although I was confident that it wouldn't have been valid in any event, I tried to assuage some of the anger I felt after her death by reminding myself that my mother had reconsidered her decision to disinherit me and destroyed the document. Since my mother was then intestate, I became the administrator of her estate by a court order.

According to the law that governs the property of people who die without a Will, Kevin and I were entitled to equal shares of my mother's assets. Neil, who had never been adopted by my mother, was not entitled to anything. Kevin and Neil both felt that we ought to disregard the law and divide my mother's estate three ways. I was still angry and didn't agree. I believed that it was somehow fitting that they should share Kevin's half of the estate. I knew that distribution wasn't fair but I was misguided. I wanted to make a statement and I didn't care.

In the end, my anger petered out and I did consent to share my mother's estate equally with Kevin and Neil. Strangely enough, it was my mother's notes that helped to end my fury. The notes were objective evidence that my mother was ill. Her hatred towards me was a construct of dementia and not what she really believed. As I read and reread her words, I finally understood that my mother had needed to blame me for what was happening in order to hold on to her vision of the old Mamie Winstanley from Campbellford, the strong and independent woman of her dreams. As Dylan Thomas urged, she was simply doing her best to "rage against the dying of the light."

The notes were my mother's final gift to me.

With the passage of time, I also understand that the roles my brothers and I assumed during my mother's battle with dementia were scripted long before her illness. Decades of family dysfunction and strained relationships set the stage for our actions and reactions during those difficult years.

My understanding doesn't come without questions or regrets. I often speculate about why Kevin and I were never close – perhaps because my childhood temper tantrums were the antithesis of his quiet and contained responses. Perhaps he resented that my mother always wanted to give me the things that she hadn't had as a child. After my mother died he told me that he found my reactions unpredictable, but that doesn't seem to explain our problems. I tell myself now that it doesn't really matter why we don't get along. We just don't.

I still wonder if I could have done something to prevent my mother's change of attitude towards me. What if I had made an effort to reconcile with Kevin before dementia struck? What if Jeff and I hadn't left Falcon Lake and bought our own cottage at Victoria Beach? What if my mother hadn't had pneumonia and I hadn't taken her to see Dr. Kalansky? What if I had recognized the signs of her illness sooner? Sometimes, I think back even farther and wonder if my mother's end would have been different if I hadn't become her ally so many years before. What if I had never been her confidante and her protector? Certainly my relationship with Neil would have been more positive and I might have sought, and received, his support during my mother's illness.

Ultimately, I know that I couldn't have done anything to avert dementia's symptoms. The illness was stronger than me; I could no more pry my mother from its grasp than I could defy the laws of gravity. I think and I hope that I did the best I could for her.

Sometimes I study the small red moles that have begun to dot my body. My mother developed those same moles as she grew older and I worry that I am destined to suffer her same fate. I have fought cancer. I have fought dementia. I know which I would choose to be my last opponent.

# Acknowledgments

WRITING IS A solitary endeavour but many people contribute to a finished manuscript. I am grateful for the love and support I received from my family and friends as I struggled my way through this project.

Thank you to my readers: Cindy Streifler, John Harvie, Melinda Tallin, Orma Gray, Judy Elliot, Andie Solomon and Anne MacKay. Their encouragement and helpful suggestions were invaluable.

Thank you to Brenlee Carrington Trepel who pointed me in the right direction.

Thank you to Sandra Lorange who gently prodded me to keep writing.

Thank you to Allyson Latta for her sage advice.

Thank you to Rhonda Bruchanski, Marianne Smith and the creative team at TAG who produced a wonderful cover and layout design as well as to my copy editor, Sherry Kaniuga.

Thank you to my much needed support team: Diane Jones, Jill Carr, Marta Smith, Vivian Hilder, Vivian Rachlis, Meryle Johnston, Esther Hirsch and Eleanor Wiebe. Good friends are so important.

Thank you to my wonderful editor and friend, Arvel Gray, who believed in my project. With wisdom, patience and humour, she helped me bring an idea to life. It is trite, but true, to say that I would not have been able to do it without her.

Thank you to my son, Davis, who inspired me to complete the final revisions to my manuscript ("of course you're going to finish"). He made my life worth fighting for so many years ago and has given me joy every day since. My mother would be so proud of the man he has become.

Finally, thank you to my husband, Jeff, who has been my soulmate, sidekick, caregiver, protector, cheerleader, best friend and so much more, in sickness and in health, for almost 32 years. Not surprisingly, he supported, encouraged, critiqued and praised my manuscript as required. He truly is perfect.

*Credit: Ian McCausland Photography*

Elizabeth Murray is a retired lawyer who lives
in Winnipeg with her husband, son and two
poodles. **Holding on to Mamie** is her first book.

www.holdingontomamie.ca

A portion of the proceeds from the sale of this book will be donated to organizations dedicated to supporting families who live with dementia.